D1067823

BULLFIGHT

PETER BUCKLEY

BONANZA BOOKS • NEW YORK

*This edition published by Bonanza Books,
a division of Crown Publishers, Inc.,
by arrangement with the author.
(B)*

LIBRARY OF CONGRESS CATALOG CARD NUMBER: 58-11806
MANUFACTURED IN THE UNITED STATES OF AMERICA

Contents

Introduction

IN THE TEXT I have chosen events to indicate the scope of the bullfight. A total view of the world of the bullfight, if only for a day, would involve a far greater complex of motion than is apparent here.

The names of the men are fictional, their actions real. They move through a day which is in no way exceptional to them. There is no history here, no technical essay, nor is the personality of any living matador of importance. These are the men who cross Spain and who give meaning to the world of the bullfight.

The photographs serve to extend and complement the view of the bullfight given in the text. The photographs are of living men who during the past ten years have appeared in the bull rings of Spain. Their identities are given in a list with brief comments; however, their names are of no concern here.

In word and photograph I have attempted to give an existence to the bullfight as it has been repeated through centuries in the late afternoon.

To César Girón, who has always been generous in his help, for his interest in this book, my thanks.

To Antonio Ordóñez, who has taught me the most, for his hospitality and the memories of San Fermin 1957, my thanks.

To the best aficionado, my friend Juanito Quintana, an *abrazo*.

P. B.

PROLOGUE

SPAIN is the stage for the bullfight from early spring until the fall. Moving in an annual rhythm, a world comes into existence in March, a closed world of constant motion whose focus is found only in the circle of the arena when the bullfight begins. From city to city the great ferias* succeed one another through the months and are fixed by the calendar: Sevilla, Jerez, Madrid, Córdoba, Granada, Burgos, Pamplona, Valencia, Vitoria, Málaga, San Sebastian, Bilbao, Palencia, Albacete, Salamanca, Valladolid, Logroño, Barcelona, Zaragoza.

The Virgin and the saints are worshiped: La Virgen Blanca, La Virgen de la Merced, La Virgen del Pilar, San José, San Isidro, San Fermin.

The bullfight is held against the changing background of city and date. During the summer the order remains but the tempo increases. The men move more quickly, and by September the climax is reached. For two hours in the late afternoon at the bullfight their travels are suspended; the bulls are in the arena and the drama is given. The men are brought together by the bullfight, only to split apart and meet again. The men belong to the bullfight. They create a world in which they live alone.

They live in a world of hotels and cars, of telephones and telegrams, and of people met on the way. It is a world of long trips at night, of late arrivals and quick departures. There are great courage and cowardice and money. There are honor and theft, those who have reached the top and those with hope.

Across Spain the cars trace an unbroken pattern from city to city and the men move with precision from bull ring to hotel, from the Carlton and the María Cristina in the north to the Miramar and the Palace in the south.

Separate units exist within the pattern. Banderilleros, picadors, drivers, sword handlers, manager, all function in direct relation to the matador and form the cuadrilla. The ranch owner finds expression in the bravery and power of his bulls. Critic and photographer are paid to praise. The impresario coordinates the action of the matadors, their men and the bulls. The doctors are in attendance at the ring.

There are those who assist the managers, the doctors, the impresarios. There are butchers, horse contractors, ushers, and the men who make the tools, the capes, the swords, the pics, the banderillas; and the women who embroider gold on silk. There are men who do nothing and want to join, and those who belong only because they are there.

There are living men whose names are a part of history, and men to whom fame has come in death. In the villages and cities of Spain the broken men listen and are told of the boys with faith. In faith they are committed. Only through the bulls can they succeed. Their way is marked with fear, and except in failure there will be no escape.

* A Glossary of Spanish and bullfighting terms used in the text will be found on pages 187–192.

ONE

IT IS WEDNESDAY. The city in the north has been in feria for a week. Since last Thursday there has been a bullfight every day at five o'clock in the afternoon. In the south, another feria will begin tomorrow.

It is seven o'clock in the evening.

The bullfight is over.

Six bulls are dead.

The tension has dropped, the anticipation gone. Men greet one another as if their friendship would endure, and a renewed sense of certainty accompanies their words. High above, from the balcony of an orphanage, nuns and children watch the immense crowd leave the arena. In the street below, groups of aficionados are arguing the weight of the bulls.

"The bulls were big."

"Fattened-up calves."

"No strength."

"The third one, one pic and down on the knees."

"They were good bulls, five years old."

"Not even four."

"Big."

"Big, with fat."

"It's the muscle and bone that weigh."

"The fat slows them down."

"They stick the fat on to fool you."

"When I saw Bombita, they were big and with no fat, and they didn't fall down," an old man says.

"But there aren't any like him any more."

"Romero is as good as any of them."

"Romero is the best."

"In his second bull, nothing, nothing."

"The bull was bad."

"If it's a bad bull, you make him good," the old man adds. "Like Joselito, you work."

"Nobody was ever better than Romero in his first bull. He faces the bull. He doesn't stand in profile all the time, like this Ortega kid."

"Manolo Ortega was the best today. He's better than his brother Juan."

"Manolo Ortega good! He's all show. He never dominates, never. It is not possible to listen to you."

"He's too fast, and his bulls were easy."

"The horns were like this." And the man makes a quick gesture with his two index fingers to show the inward curve of the bull's horns.

"Romero has the best wrist. If you could see with your eyes, you could see that he is better than the two Ortegas put together. He'll take a bad bull and make him good."

"Once in six months he will."

"He doesn't give a damn for the public."

"Why should he?"

"Because the public pays."

"Jiménez gives the public what they want."

"Yes, but he's not good."

"Jiménez is the best."

"Jiménez likes the bulls small."

"And he gets them small."

"His manager sees to that."

"Why do you think he's paid more than Romero? More than anyone else? Because he's the best."

"He's paid the most, sure. He's paid for stunts and easy stuff with easy bulls."

"There's the difference between Antonio Romero and Francisco Jiménez. Romero is good, and Jiménez looks good. How many people know the difference?"

"Jiménez is the best. He's better than anyone else ever was. If he'd been here he would have made Romero look like the fake he is. Two ears for that faena. It's a joke. Jiménez tries!"

"Jiménez the best? Romero gives you more in one day than Jiménez in a year. Salamanca bulls, that's all Jiménez ever fights!"

"He's fighting Conde de la Corte bulls tomorrow with Romero and Manolo Ortega."

"Where?"

"In the south."

"Jiménez won't do anything. He'll be too scared."

"Jiménez is vulgar. He steals your money."

"Romero is a fraud."

"Manolo Ortega is new, but he's good. He's got Romero's wrist and he dominates like his brother Juan. You saw it today."

"Big names! They give nothing. The novilladas are better. I never miss one."

"Manolo Ortega is worth nothing."

"With the cape he's good, but he kills badly."

"He'll be better than Romero and Jiménez tomorrow. He's not afraid of the Conde de la Corte bulls."

"Wait till he feels the horn, then we'll see."

"He can get the horn and still be good. Did you see the wound his brother Juan got in Burgos? Four with the left, the best he ever gave, the best in anybody; *paf, paf, paf, paf,* one, two, three, four, and he gets it here." The man slaps his inner left thigh. "Up he goes. When he twisted back down, I thought he was dead. It looked worse than the one that killed Jiménez' brother."

"The worst ones never look bad."

"It was bad. That was three and a half weeks ago, and he fought today with Jiménez and that disaster Posada."

"Posada wasn't so bad the first year. He's like most of them. He wasn't like Belmonte, like some people said. No one's ever like Belmonte, but Posada was good. He could have been very good. A little like Pepe Luis, then he gets it, and ever since—nothing. If he does get near the bull, it scares you to death."

"I didn't like the horses," an American says.

"That padding doesn't help much."

"Sure doesn't. I wonder how the guy is who got gored."

"Looked bad."

"I don't know."

"What's his name?"

"He was in blue, wasn't he?"

"Yeah."

"You still have that program?"

"He fought second, didn't he?"

"Yeah."

"The heavy one, first, was he in green?"

"Yeah."

"That's Romero."

"And it wasn't the kid. He was good, four ears and a tail. We were lucky."

"Must have been Cascales, then. Sure, he was the guy you threw the flowers to. What'd you do it for? He didn't look so good."

"He reminded me of Pete. I liked him."

"Come on, let's go see if there's any mail."

"You know, I heard all the bulls are virgins."

"Come on, let's go, will you?"

"Ça t'a plu, chérie?"

"Oui, mais c'est assez facile ce qu'ils font. Il suffit de bien connaître la mentalité du taureau."

"Ah, non, chérie, tu te trompes. T'a vu le gars qui s'est fait encorné?"

"Oui."

"Eh, bien."

"Eh, bien, quoi? Il était bête, c'est tout. Il n'y a pas tellement de danger là-dedans. Tu pourrais en faire autant, tu sais. C'est une question de s'y mettre."

"Manolo Ortega was good, yes, but I have to see him with a bull to know. He could be good. He could be as good as Joselito. The year before Joselito was killed I saw him in thirty-eight bullfights. Thirty-eight. The seats were cheap then. You could get a good *abono* for twenty-six pesetas. You two wouldn't remember."

"Yes, Don Mariano."

"The toreros today aren't the men they used to be. They haven't got them any more." Don Mariano handles himself to illustrate. "This Cascales. He is worth nothing. No personality. Nothing to remember."

Don Mariano Martín steps into his new Jaguar sedan. Don Mariano lives in Valencia. He owns immense lands near Murcia, where he raises and cans fruits and vegetables which he ships to the entire world. He is accompanied by his two young local representatives.

"I saw Joselito thirty-eight times in one year—most of the time with Belmonte—and with *bulls.* The bullfight was for men. There was no sentimentality. The stands weren't full of women. Pretty men and pretty passes is all they can see, and if the man is caught on the horn they cringe and shriek and tell you it's savage. I don't care what they think. They have brought their nursery feelings into the Plaza, and it's rubbed off onto their men. Do you think that forty years ago the public in this city would have accepted the bulls we saw today? Do you think the toreros would have fought these bulls? They had pride. Lagartijo, Guerrita, they would have been ashamed to be seen with these bulls."

"The bulls didn't look small, Don Mariano."

"The weight was there, but the years were not. A five-year-old-bull demands everything a man has, and the man does not have to fake and make it look hard, because if does he'll get killed. He has no time for stunts. He's got to protect himself and try to create a faena before the bull knows too much. At five, the bull gives the man a chance to show what he's got, but the man has to know and then do it, or else he'll look bad—if he's lucky. If he's not lucky, he goes to the doctor. There's no room for a mistake. Joselito was the finest matador who ever lived. He made one mistake at Talavera de la Reina and died. It's with the years the bull gets hard and learns. This afternoon there was no strength, no resistance in the legs. They all came to the muleta with their tongues out. Sure, the weight was there, and you think it was a bull, and the public thinks it was a bull. Give a sixteen-year-old boy another forty pounds, it doesn't make him a man of thirty. There wasn't a horse thrown. The picadors sat up there on top of the mattress and murdered the bulls. They were as safe with those bulls as we are in the car. It's the mattress that lets them assassinate the bulls. The matador wants the picador to kill the bull, and he tells him to do it, and then later he pays the fine, and the next day it's the same. The mattress is there to protect the public, not the horse. What it comes to is that the bullfight is something else now. Sixty fancy passes with every bull. It is impossible, but it's what the public wants, and they don't know the difference between a good kill and a bad kill because they never saw a good one, and the matadors don't bother because they know that a good kill is the most dangerous act."

Don Mariano rolls up the window. "You like the new car? It's better than my Buick." Don Mariano wears an emerald ring. He has fought for the lands and factories he owns. "I was three years old when my father took me to my first bullfight."

The crowd moves slowly and without purpose. Immediately ahead there is beer, wine, coffee, lemonade in the cafés and hotels. Three blind men jab at a hedge with their canes, trying to find an opening which will lead them from an open area to a row of buildings. In single file eight bowlegged dwarfs push through the knees of the crowd on their way to a bar. In the street, on one side of the arena, lines are forming in front of open booths, to buy tickets for the Comic Taurine performance to be given tonight at eleven o'clock by the eight dwarfs, four clowns and a local boy trying to attract attention. The dwarfs and the clowns are the main attraction, and the men will buy tickets for their wives and children to see the deformed and ludicrous. A full house will please the impresarios, the dwarfs and the clowns. The local boy will wish the stands empty if he has a disaster and will be glad they are full if has a triumph in his single fight with a yearling bull. Now the boy is sitting in his mother's kitchen, afraid.

The sun has gone down and the air is cool. The crowd has left the Plaza de Toros temporarily empty. A twelve-year-old boy descends from high up in the stands, from where he has seen his sixth bullfight. He saw the first three by sneaking into the arena when he was seven and eight years old. After that, his sudden growth made him more noticeable to the ushers, who caught him and kicked him when he fought back. He missed the next four bullfights in town, and then stole money from his father's fruit and vegetable stand in the market place. In this way he saw his fourth and fifth bullfights. His father beat him harder than the ushers and threw him into the street for a month. His mother fed him late at night, after his father had gone to bed, permitting him to sleep in the cellar, and got him up early in the morning before his father awoke.

Today the boy was lucky. An Englishman whose wife had missed her train on the way to join him gave the boy his extra ticket. It was an expensive seat on the shady side in the third row, but the boy had preferred to sit in the sun alone. He remembered another man who had offered him beer in a café and a ticket. He had had to run and miss the bullfight.

Reaching the empty ring of sand below, the boy jumps into the narrow corridor that circles the arena and slips his body through the barrera. He stands alone, inside the ring itself, and then walks straight across and out the other side.

A crowd is watching the sixth bull being butchered. The first five carcasses are cleaned and hanging overhead, ready to be sent to the market. The boy wishes he could steal a pair of horns, but the fat *mayoral* is watching, a thin riding crop held in one hand. The boy's older brother warned him at breakfast: If he did not bring home a pair of horns, he would not be allowed to join the group at the bullfight school where the horns are needed for practice. The Englishman appears, speaks to the *mayoral* and the head butcher; he does not see the boy, and he leaves with the largest pair of horns, the ones the boy wants most. The Englishman heads for a café, thinking how well the horns will look over the cocktail bar in his new flat.

The boy follows him, and the ushers collect their cushions in the empty stands, store them and go home. The picadors' horses are led to the stables, their protective mattresses dumped in a storeroom. The horse contractor leaves.

Through the great iron gates of the Plaza de Toros the crowd has surged into the city. In the main square, a dense mass of men and boys are carrying Manolo Ortega on their shoulders. Across the square and through the street the fans are running. In triumph the matador is held above the crowd and can be seen from a distance. Ahead, the crowd parts to make way for Manolo Ortega. An ovation follows the procession and moves in rhythm with the passage of the young matador. Manolo Ortega is eighteen and a half years old.

"Manolo, Manolo, Manolo.

"Manolo Ortega.

"Manolo, Manolo, Manolo.

"Manolo Ortega."

The smooth side of the right horn of Manolo Ortega's first bull has left the matador's lower abdomen bruised and burning from a glancing blow. In his second faena he almost fell when a badly placed banderilla hit him in the groin. Hoping to sit back in the cuadrilla's large car on the way to the hotel, he fought the fans who jumped into the ring to carry him out in triumph. He gave in, too weak to resist the crowd, and he has become nauseated jogging on their shoulders.

The three men who are holding Manolo Ortega are running. On all sides they are jolted by those who want to reach the matador. Men from the city join the mass of hurrying, stumbling men in a desire to become a part of the triumph. Manolo Ortega's name is shouted in praise, and the matador waves his arms in a lurching attempt to accept the crowd's devotion and to keep from falling.

During the past month Manolo Ortega has traveled 11,120 miles and fought in twenty-six bullfights. He has killed fifty-five bulls, cut thirty-nine ears, eleven tails, and two hoofs, to make the success more spectacular. A year ago Manolo Ortega was unknown. In the cities in which he has appeared this season, Manolo Ortega has become the center of discussion. He will appear next year in these cities and his manager will negotiate a better contract. His fame has grown, and in the ferias ahead Manolo Ortega is expected.

A pack of small boys follows the matador. Leaping from behind, they scramble through the crowd and announce Manolo Ortega to those ahead. Traffic stops, the crowd turns the corner, men and women stand on their chairs in the cafés to see Manolo Ortega. The matador clutches for support, falls backward, and is raised up again.

A crowd is waiting in front of the hotel. The running mass of men and boys merges with the crowd and stops. The street is filled. Manolo Ortega's feet touch the ground and he runs inside.

In his room Manolo Ortega strips, flops into bed under a sheet, and places a call to his brother, Juan Ortega, in the east. "Get it through quickly. I'm leaving."

He replaces the receiver on the telephone cradle. His right hand is caked with blood. It was a good kill, and as the sword sank to the hilt, Manolo Ortega's left arm crossed perfectly with the muleta, taking the horns away from his body. As he came out, his sword hand brushed the pumping wound made by the pics.

In the bath, the hot water burns his scraped flesh. His shoulder muscles ache, they are tight as stones. For weeks they have felt like this. For weeks Manolo Ortega has been better than Antonio Romero.

From the bull ring to the hotel, a boy rode on top of Antonio Romero's car. He sat next to the great leather basket that holds the capotes and muletas. The boy touched the fresh blood on the muletas with one hand while he held onto the baggage rack with the other. When the car stopped, the boy jumped down and opened the door for Antonio Romero. The crowd watched the matador step across the yard of sidewalk into the de luxe hotel lobby. Antonio Romero has killed 1,046 bulls in his life. He is twenty-five years old.

Antonio Romero undresses, puts on the bathrobe his wife gave him and lies down to rest. The matador is tall, strong and confident that he is the best. Within an hour he must leave for the south of Spain.

Antonio Romero spent the years from the age of five to sixteen playing with the calves and working with the bulls. He lived on the ranches and grew to know the bulls. He studied the technique of a single pass for months until technique and knowledge became instinctive. When he was sixteen, Antonio Romero learned to read. At nineteen he took the alternativa after three years as a novillero. His fame has never rested upon the spectacular. Through the years he has grown in stature. With difficulty he has resisted the increasing tendency in his profession to replace the truth with the flamboyant. He has remained faithful to the classical norms of the bullfight, and his role has been made more exacting by this decision. Until today, the respect given him as an artist is universal among men who know the bullfight.

Antonio Romero dominates the bull with elegance and style. He can temper a bull's charge with rhythm. He has the courage to receive the horns while standing motionless and to kill as well and with as much honor as any man.

As he watched Manolo Ortega in the ring, Antonio Romero recalled the early years when he had had to fight better every day to reach the top. At times it is worse to be the best. When you are third-rate and you do two decent passes, the crowd is surprised and pleased, but if you are the best, and you do twenty good passes, the finest they've seen in ten years, and it looks easy because you are the best, they like it, but they expect it, and more. When there is no more, not because you don't want to give it, but because there is no more to give except to be killed, you quit trying to please the crowd and start to work for yourself, your friends, and those who know, and you hope you are enough on top to stay there.

During the spring, summer and fall, for nine years, Antonio Romero has traveled across Spain. In the winter he has crossed the Atlantic and fought in South and Central America. He has promised his wife to stop in three years. His son will become a matador and will follow his father and grandfather into the bull rings of Spain.

The matador's sword handler runs a bath and finishes packing the suitcases. The room is full: manager, city official, photographer, critic, ranch owner, impresario, reporters, unknowns, men who are old friends, men who want to become old friends, local enthusiasts, men who can help, and those who want to be helped. Antonio Romero is resting. He is tired. A constant traffic of men and women enters the room.

The third matador, Julio Cascales, has not left the bull ring. The wound in his thigh is slight, but it must be cleaned and sewed. No contracts have to be canceled, because there are no contracts. The painful lights above the operating table force him to close his eyes. The forceps remove a gold thread which the horn ripped from his trousers and embedded in the first layer of muscle.

Cascales thinks of Domingo Vasquez, who is lying in a Barcelona hospital with a deep two-trajectory wound in the abdomen and lung which could still prove fatal. If Vasquez were not in the hospital he would have fought here today, and Cascales would have taken a walk or sat in his café at home in Albacete. Aficionados pay to see Vasquez. The impresarios had been certain, when they heard that Vasquez might die of the wound suffered forty-eight hours earlier, that a call to Cascales would bring him quickly to their ring and for one third the price offered Vasquez. The ring would probably fill anyway, with Antonio Romero and Manolo Ortega.

This month Cascales has traveled one way from Albacete to the north to one fight in which he cut nothing, and is now going home to wait for someone else's bad luck or some impresario who wants a matador, cheap.

Suerte—if I had only had luck, Cascales thinks, as the wound is being bandaged. Manolo Ortega didn't need four ears and a tail this afternoon. Ever since his alternativa six weeks ago he has had luck. He has more luck in an hour than I have in a year. He doesn't need contracts. If I had a tenth of his contracts at his prices, I could buy the farm and quit waiting.

Maybe the crowd liked me. There was no bronca when the sword hit bone and slipped sideways and out the shoulder blade. The crowd understood it can happen to anyone. They must have liked me. They insulted Romero during his second faena, and he's the best. They never yelled at me like that. I heard a woman yell *"olé"* when I tried the pendulum. It didn't work well, my legs ducked back, but I couldn't help it. I tried, and she yelled *"olé."* The crowd liked me. There was applause when my second bull was dragged out. It was for the bull, but the bull wouldn't have got the applause if I hadn't made him look good. There wasn't a pass I didn't try. I even thought of attempting an arrucina, but they couldn't have known that. I would have done it if the bull hadn't hooked left all the time. If I had tried, he would have emptied me on the sand. I'm lucky I only got this. Romero never would have done what I did with that bull. He would have cut him down, chop, chop, chop, tire him, twist him, hurt him, in for the kill, running off to the left in case the bull hooked right.

I went in over the horns. He hooked to the left, and it was easy. Straight over the right horn and four times, bone, bone, bone, bone. I always get bone. Manolo Ortega, he gets butter, rich butter, butter luck. The sword slips into his bulls as if the damned bulls just decided to melt when they see Manolo coming. His bulls melt their bones down until only the marrow butter is left for the sword. Anybody can be great with that luck. There were only a few whistles at me. Some people in the barrera smiled, and a girl threw me a bouquet. She didn't look Spanish, and somebody yelled at her to save the flowers for Manolo Ortega, but still she threw them. I hope Cano got a picture of me with the flowers. It'll look good in the ad with full stands in the background. I'll ask him if he got it.

The wound aches, but it is clean and bandaged, and as the doctor prepares to meet his friends in the café, Cascales is helped from the operating table into his car. The twenty-eight-year-old matador returns to the hotel.

There is no crowd at the hotel to surround Cascales when he enters at 7:20. The elevator boy does not ask if the wound is serious. The matador's room is empty.

Across the hall an American photographer is trying to introduce a Yale boy to Antonio Romero. The Yale boy is sure he can be good if the matador will only tell him what to do. He has been in Spain for three years, waiting. His sports convertible carries him from one bullfight to another. He wants to become a matador. The photographer once sold some pictures of Antonio Romero to *Vogue*. He has met the matador before and has made three dates to have cocktails with him, but the matador has not appeared. He accepted the invitations because it is polite to say yes. The photographer was angry because he had promised his friends that they would meet the matador, and he had decided never to speak to Antonio Romero again.

The matador's friends, the ones who like Antonio Romero and the ones Antonio Romero likes, are sitting close to him on the bed or standing quietly at a distance talking among themselves.

At the door, a French industrialist forces his way into the packed room. He feels an obligation to speak to Antonio Romero, to tell him that his veronicas suffer from improper timing.

A young woman with a large, flat package enters the room, pushes toward the bed, sits on it and unwraps her package. Antonio Romero has never seen her before. From the package the woman pulls seven water colors of Antonio Romero. One is a portrait, and six show the matador in the ring, facing a black-and-white bull. Antonio Romero is afraid of black-and-white bulls. His best banderillero is in the Madrid Sanatorio de Toreros because of a black-and-white bull. The matador looks at the seven paintings. The French industrialist stands next to the bed eagerly trying to see. Telling the woman that her work is lovely, the matador hands the paintings over to the Frenchman. The pictures serve the Frenchman as a conversational link with the matador. *"J'ai deux Lautrecs chez moi qui me font souvent penser à la corrida. Vous savez, matador, que les mouvements dans le cirque de Lautrec sont presque les mêmes que dans l'arène."*

The French industrialist shoves the wrapping paper, which covers the bed, onto the floor and sits between the woman and a good friend of Antonio Romero's. Putting his hand on the matador's arm, the Frenchman says, *"Écoutez, mon cher ami, vos véroniques sont très bien, mais . . . "*

The matador's friend stands up. He has been squeezed against the bedstead by the Frenchman; he does not understand French any more than Romero and he says, "I am going, Antonio, *me voy.*"

The matador is tense. "Stay!" he says to his friend. "Don't go!" And he whispers and indicates the industrialist. "Pedro," he calls to his sword handler, handing him the paintings, "take care of this!"

"Don't you want them, matador?" the woman inquires. "You said you liked them. They are only five hundred pesetas each."

"See Pedro!" the matador answers.

She follows her paintings to the door, and the Frenchman is edged out after her by the matador's friend. A waiter enters with coffee and brandy for Romero just as the Frenchman reaches the hall. The friend enlists the waiter, who speaks some French, into explaining that the matador kills bulls, speaks Spanish, and is tired. Leaving the waiter to listen to a critique on the finer aspects of the verónica, the friend re-enters the room. He gathers up the paper and string, throws them into the waste basket, and serves the coffee and brandy to Antonio Romero.

The American photographer has brought the Yale boy to the matador's attention. Antonio Romero has no interest in furthering the careers of foreigners, yet his answer is courteous. He introduces the Yale boy to a friend who owns a bull-breeding ranch near Sevilla. The rancher extends an invitation to attend the tientas which will take place next spring.

As they leave, the Yale boy turns to the photographer and says, "I want to learn how to make the passes. Why the hell should I go and play with a bunch of calves? Does he think I'm afraid? I've been to those things. I want to know how to do a pedresina or an arrucina." And he names a half-dozen extravagant and suicidal passes, most of which have been well executed only by their inventors.

From the lobby, Antonio Romero's driver calls upstairs. "The car is ready, matador."

"I'll be down in twenty minutes."

Antonio Romero jiggles the receiver and asks the operator to hurry the call he has put through to his wife in Madrid.

In another part of the city, near the harbor, Manolo Ortega's driver is filling the matador's car with gas. A cold mist is moving in from the Atlantic.

The city could be San Sebastián, Bilbao, Santander, Gijón, La Coruña, in the north.

It is 7:30 in the evening.

TWO

IN ANOTHER CITY, in the east on the Mediterranean coast, the crowds are filling the cafés. It is hot. Three huge cars are waiting, their motors turning, as the matadors leave the bull ring. Francisco Jiménez, the highest-paid matador in Spain, is the first to reach his car. He has instantly left the arena and avoided the men who had hoped to carry him through the city in triumph. Jiménez pushes through the clamoring crowd, staring ahead, seeing no one. Helped by his driver, Jiménez sits in the back seat between two of his banderilleros as the thirty-year-old Rolls Royce leaves the Plaza de Toros.

Francisco Jiménez has been well paid for his vulgar bravery and apparent disdain of death. The crowd cheered loudly when Jiménez knelt on the sand in front of his first bull and looked up defiantly at the horns three feet above his motionless body. The crowd did not know that the bull could not see Francisco Jiménez, that as long as the bull's head is raised he can see nothing directly in front for some nine feet.

The good aficionados had watched Jiménez in disgust. Awkwardly Jiménez faced the bull on his knees, turned his back to the bull on his knees, and then standing up, he stumbled away to pick up the sword and muleta he had thrown aside with bravado before starting his series of stunts. The crowd was moved and responded with an ovation.

Jiménez is capable of the truth, but both he and his manager recognize that the public pays. "Give them the adornos—the tricks—they want 'em. The ones who know don't fill a hundred seats," the manager has said repeatedly.

"Open the windows. It's hot," the matador says to his sword handler and manager, who are sitting in front of him.

The street is full. Hands and arms crowd into the windows, reach across the banderilleros and touch the matador, touch his pink-and-gold suit, touch his skin, feel his hands, feel his face, slap his shoulders. The car stops, surrounded. Faces follow the hands through the windows, yelling.

"Jiménez, *Machote*."

"Jiménez, Jiménez!"

"Machote! Machote!"

"You are a man. Yours are like this!" And a globe is formed with two hands.

"You are the greatest!"

"Francisco, Francisco!"

"Paco!"

"How are you, my friend?"

"My friend, Francisco Jiménez."

"There are no better than you."

"Jiménez, *Jiménez!*"

The hands and voices fill the Rolls Royce.

Jiménez is smoking. The banderilleros, the manager, and the sword handler stare ahead, waiting for the car to move. The men who cannot reach the matador touch the driver, speak to him, touch the three banderilleros, the manager, the sword handler, ask them intimate questions, tell them the answers, feel them, grab them and shout. Those who cannot reach inside touch the fenders of the car in which the matador sits. Those who cannot speak to the men inside the car speak to those who are outside and touch the men who are touching Jiménez.

Two men admire the tires on the car. "They are the best tires. They cost a lot of money. Jiménez deserves these tires." They feel the tires and disregard the wheels when they start to move. A lucky hand slaps Jiménez' face.

"Shut the windows," Jiménez orders quietly. "Give me a handkerchief." The car moves faster. The sword handler gives the matador a clean white handkerchief. Jiménez wipes his face.

The crowd that accompanies Emilio Posada and the Guardia Civil from the arena to the car is dangerous. Those who are unable to glorify Jiménez defy and insult Posada.

"*Sin vergüenza*, without shame."

[TEXT CONTINUES ON PAGE 25.]

RESTAURANTE DELIC
URANTE
M-27549
S.P.

20A

20B

24 A

24 B

"Sin vergüenza, sin vergüenza!"

"Go and steal in another city!"

"Get out of here and don't come back!"

"Coward!"

"Fairy!"

"Thief!"

"Sneak!"

"Butcher!"

"You have no shame!"

"Defrauder!"

A foot trips Emilio Posada, matador de toros. He starts to fall and the instant the Guardia steady him, Posada is cruelly hit in the face by a raised knee and jabbed in the groin with a beer bottle. The Guardia drag the matador through the crowd, intent upon getting rid of their duty. The car door is open. Posada is pushed into the back seat. The doors are locked and the windows closed. The car moves dangerously through the crowd.

Juan Ortega ignores the men who attempt to reach him, men shouting *"Machote,* Ortega, you are the best." Men trying to touch his skin, men trying to be near him because he has not been too afraid this afternoon and has had some luck. Juan Ortega is hot, but he orders the windows closed and his driver to drive. "Forget the crowd," he adds, seeing Posada's car surrounded on his left. "Let's get out. Forget 'em, drive."

A young girl, excited by the bulls, the crowd, the heat, the toreros, waves at Juan Ortega as his car passes her. He quickly puts the window down and smiles.

"Come and join my cuadrilla," he shouts. "Come, *guapa,* come on, come, *venga."* The girl runs after the car.

"Make her run, Juan," the *banderillero de confianza* says.

Juan Ortega leans out of the window. "Come on, run, run, *guapa,* run." He can still see the crowd surrounding Posada's car. "Come on, run," he shouts. "Run, run." The girl is full, she is pretty, she runs. "It will make you strong, run!"

"She'll break you in her legs, matador, if you make her run like that," the *banderillero de confianza* adds, grinning.

"Break me, *guapa,* break me in your legs!" Juan Ortega shouts back. The girl runs quickly through the thick crowd. "Drive, go on, drive," he shouts at his driver. "Break me, *guapa."* The matador howls in false agony.

The pretty girl runs. She steps on a pair of crutches lying beside a beggar without legs, twists painfully and falls into the dirt among the feet of the crowd.

"Ha, see, she's lying down for you, Juanito," the matador's manager says, laughing.

"*Guapa, guapa,* my pretty one, run," Juan Ortega shouts. "The one with crutches can't do it for you." And the matador laughs and closes his window. The beggar viciously pushes the girl away from where his legs should be and grabs at his crutches to see if they are broken.

"If I was afraid like Posada, I'd stop," Juan Ortega says to his cuadrilla. "I couldn't go on, even for the money—I couldn't. He can't bring himself within a mile of the horns. For God's sake, I'm afraid every afternoon, but I get over it—it hasn't got me like him; it makes you more afraid, just to see him—and he's fighting here tomorrow. I'm glad I'm not on the cartel. He should quit."

Just before the car reaches the hotel, Juan Ortega tells his driver to be ready in an hour. "We're leaving early. I'll have dinner in the next town and have fun tonight." As he rides up in the elevator with his sword handler, Juan Ortega flicks the elevator boy's ear with his fingernail. It hurts the boy, but he turns around and smiles. "Too bad you missed the bullfight," the matador says, flicking the boy's ear again. "I was good."

On the third floor, Emilio Posada is in the bathroom. "The damn bulls won't charge. They never charge any more. Stand with their stupid ears twitching, looking at me, not charging, looking, looking at me, waiting for me to walk over so that they can stick me full of their filthy splintered horns. The horns aren't even clean, covered with dung from the other bulls . . . "

Emilio Posada has not stopped talking since getting into a bath. Neither his manager nor his sword handler is paying the slightest attention to a word he is saying. One sits smoking on the bed, the other is examing one of the matador's shoes to see if the bull damaged it when he stepped on the matador's foot.

Too bad he didn't fracture his foot, then he wouldn't have to fight tomorrow, the sword handler thinks.

He hasn't been paid in a month.

"My foot hurts, Don Manuel," Posada yells. "The hot water makes it sting. Look at it!"

The manager smokes. When Posada was seventeen, Don Manuel had been lucky to get him. Every manager in Spain wanted Emilio Posada, phenomenon extraordinary, rising novillero, ears and tails and hoofs in easy provincial towns, inventor of flashy passes in impossible terrains, the new Manolete, the Belmonte, the sensation of the century. The day he'd signed Posada for five years and had gone out and got drunk with the millions they were going to make, the manager had been the envy of everybody. "A percentage of Posada, why that's like having a percentage of government graft," someone had told him. "And there's nothing easier nor surer nor fatter than graft in a country that belongs to the government."

"It's like having a piece of heaven on paper," his brother had said when he'd seen the contract.

His wife had been glad for the new jewelry, the new servants to do for her what she had always done for herself. His son had been glad for the work he didn't have to do any more—which he had never done seriously, hoping his father would land a phenomenon of the century, a phenomenon just like Emilio Posada, idol of the crowds, gold mine.

Posada was going up, up, up, to the top, and he was good, and the crowds paid to fill the stands every day he fought. Posada would not get killed, not for a while, not till a lot of all the money was in. The first small money—it looked small only when compared to what was coming—was spent on necessities that had never been needed. Posada rose faster and higher than the manager and the manager's family and new friends and Posada's new friends had even hoped. Within two months Posada rose from a novillero who had fought twenty times in the preceding season to a novillero with eighty-two contracts in four months, eighty-two bullfights in one hundred and twenty days. The manager had been disappointed when he realized that not even his sensation could fill any more contracts. The faster the money came in, the better it would be. Posada rose higher, and the impresarios were forced to pay more, if they wanted the phenomenon to fill their stands with ecstatic crowds. "My foot hurts, the soap stings, look," the matador is saying in his bath.

On the day he took the alternativa five years ago, Posada had reached the top, and a hundred contracts lay ahead. His second bull gave him a deep three-trajectory wound which descended the length of his right thigh to the knee, and rose when his weight swung back down on the horn into the abdomen. Posada suffered no pain on the horn. The doctor's report in the papers the next day gave the details. All contracts were canceled. Another rising sensation replaced Emilio Posada.

One great fight in this town three months ago, and Posada's manager had talked the impresario into putting Posada on three days in a row during the feria, for very little, one tenth the fee he got five years ago.

"He's going to the top again, the top," the manager had said. The impresario had signed because it was for so little. He'd put Juan Ortega and Francisco Jiménez on the same bill and probably fill the Plaza. Somebody'd come, thinking Posada might go to the top again, and they'd fill the other seats. It would be all right, and maybe Posada might have luck. He might even be good. It was worth the chance, at the price.

With the toes of his unhurt foot, Posada turns the cold-water faucet at the end of the bath. Maybe putting his bruised foot under the cold water will make the swelling go down. He has asked the manager's opinion but the manager has not answered.

"They charged for Jiménez and Ortega, why can't they charge for me?" Posada asks his manager. "Why can't the bulls charge?" He starts to fish under his left leg for the soap. He had told the sword handler to buy the kind of soap that floats. Gently Posada washes the scar which runs from his right knee to within a few inches of his naval.

"They *make* the bulls charge," the manager

answers, getting up from the bed in the next room. He drops his cigarette on the tile floor and walks out. The door slams.

Posada washes his scar again. He always washes the scar from the knee toward the abdomen, never the other way. "Tomorrow I'll be good," he says. "Tomorrow they'll charge. I'll be good. They'll charge straight."

Posada steps out of his bath and dries the scar with care. He is alone.

In Francisco Jiménez' room, the Duke of Valdemoro is sitting in the large armchair, relaxed, his thin legs crossed. His clothes are in impeccable taste. He speaks perfect French and English. For the past three years he has followed Francisco Jiménez throughout Spain. Already, this season, he has seen Jiménez in twenty-nine bullfights.

"You were very good today, Francisco."

"Thank you, Johnny," the matador answers.

The sword handler lights the Duke of Valdemoro's cigarette. Jiménez is undressing. His body is thin and supple. For two years the Duke of Valdemoro followed Antonio Romero throughout Spain, from bullfight to bullfight. Antonio Romero invited the Duke of Valdemoro to his wedding. The duke did not come to the wedding and began to follow Francisco Jiménez from bullfight to bullfight.

"I don't remember that scar," the duke says, pointing to the matador's inner right thigh. "It cannot be from this year, it is white."

"I got it in a tienta when I was thirteen," the matador answers shyly, "from a calf." Francisco Jiménez puts on the silk bathrobe that the Duke of Valdemoro brought him from London last spring. The matador's gestures are more graceful than they are in the ring, where the fierce, self-imposed control makes his performance angular and tense.

The sword handler places the pink-and-gold jacket over the back of a chair and packs the matador's suitcase.

Jiménez' manager walks in. "How are you, Johnny?" He sits on the bed. "Thought you'd be here. I told Don Eduardo you were."

"Is he coming up?"

"I think so. He wants to go with you to the bullfight tomorrow. He just got back from Greece, and his car is in Madrid."

"I don't know if there will be room. Francisco is coming with me tonight," the duke answers.

"I can't, Johnny," Jiménez calls from the bathroom. "Huertas and I are going to see Carmen Montoya tonight. I'll see you tomorrow. We can have dinner."

"All right, Francisco. I think I'll find Eduardo." And the duke takes his hat, which he has thrown to Francisco Jiménez in the bull rings of Spain during the past three years, whenever the matador has circled the arena in triumph. The Duke of Valdemoro throws his hat only to Francisco Jiménez.

An eager group of men enters the room as the Duke of Valdemoro leaves. Awkwardly the matador accepts their tribute. Francisco Jiménez' generosity has earned him an even larger retinue of admirers than most matadors have. An innate desire to be liked prompts him to give in the only manner he knows. The matador has few friends. He finds it impossible to become free of the flattery and worship that surround him. To reject the false praise and greed of his admirers would be to give offense. Francisco Jiménez cannot offend. Whenever a charity bullfight is planned—for which the matadors donate their service—the first to come forward is always Jiménez. In his home town he has given large sums of money to the poor.

It is extremely difficult for him to communicate. He can be at ease and tell a joke only with men he has known for a long time. He is gentle and devout. When he dances, he holds the girl at a distance and is correct in his behavior.

For a year Jiménez retired from his profession. His magnificent home is built like a hotel: bedroom, bath, bedroom, bath, bedroom, bath. Having few friends, he found during his retirement that the long corridors of his home were empty. A few months ago Jiménez came out of retirement at the age of twenty-four. Next year, he has decided, he will buy a yacht and go fishing again near his home town.

In the arena, his need to be accepted has obliged him to give the public what the public wants. But it is not merely by performing stunts that he has earned considerably more than two million dollars.

Consistently, more than anyone during the long bullfight months for the past five years, Jiménez has given the public his best. When the bulls are bad and there is nothing to be done, he tries nevertheless. He knows what the bulls can do. His own brother was killed in the arena.

Seated in a large armchair in the center of the room Francisco Jiménez listens to the pleas of the men who surround him.

The telephone rings in Juan Ortega's room. The sword handler answers and hands the phone to the matador. "Manolo."

"*Qué tal?*" Juan Ortega asks. "How are you?"

Manolo Ortega, in the north, is dressed, ready to leave. The two brothers are over four hundred miles apart. "*Bien, muy bien, Juan,*" he answers. "I cut four ears and a tail. The corrida was big. My second one was the biggest, six hundred and ten kilos, the one I got the tail on. They carried me back to the hotel." Manolo Ortega does not mention how sick he felt jogging through the streets on top of the crowd. His room is full of people. He feels all right now. The nausea is gone, and he is drinking a cup of coffee with a drop of brandy in it. "How did you do?"

"One ear," Juan answers.

"*Bien.* See you tomorrow," Manolo shouts. The telephone works well, but Manolo thinks it helps to shout.

"I'm leaving tonight, Manolo, so I'll see you when you get in. *Adiós,* Manolito, *adiós.*"

"See you about noon. *Adiós,*" Manolo answers.

THREE

IN THE NORTH, Manolo Ortega is waiting for the elevator at the end of the hall. He looks at his watch, pushes the bell impatiently and quickly forgets the time.

Downstairs, Antonio Romero is in the bar off the lobby, having a lemonade with a friend.

On the second floor, Julio Cascales answers a knock at his door. His manager stands in a corner of the room, and a friend from home sits on the bed. No one is talking. Don Mariano Martín walks in. His emerald ring catches the matador's eye. Don Mariano has sent his two local representatives out to buy him a box of fifty Montecristo cigars.

"Qué tal, matador?" Don Mariano calls out. "We are from the same part of the country. I was born in Murcia. I live in Valencia now, but I'm Murciano. You're from Albacete, aren't you?"

Cascales nods. *"Si, señor."* He stands quietly in front of his guest. The matador's shoelaces are untied.

"I'm Mariano Martín, a great *aficionado a los toros.* I saw Joselito thirty-eight times in one season —thirty-eight. He was a great friend of mine, a great friend. We were very close. You've met me before. I've seen you often in the ring, and I wanted to come to see you this evening." Don Mariano continues. "I'm a great aficionado, you know that. I gave the impresarios in Valencia their first money, the money they started with. They wanted me to come in with them, but I refused."

"With your permission, Señor Martín." The matador sits on the bed and ties his shoes.

Don Mariano makes a gesture in deference to the matador. Cascales does not speak. His friend and his manager move toward the door and stand waiting.

"I saw you two months ago in Barcelona," Don Mariano says. "You were the best that day."

Cascales knows, Don Mariano knows, the manager and the friend know that Cascales was the best in Barcelona. The four men remember also that the other two matadors had been extremely bad. Cascales triumphed only by avoiding the insane fear of the others, at whom the small crowd had shrieked in anger. Cascales tried, and the crowd showed him their appreciation by remaining silent.

This was the day to which Don Mariano refers as the best. This was Cascales' most recent fight until the horn caught Domingo Vasquez and the impresarios had telephoned him. Today had been different. The silence to which Cascales listened a few hours ago had been in violent contrast to the frenzied ovations given Manolo Ortega and the deep respect accorded Antonio Romero's excellent faena.

"Was I good today?" Cascales asks Don Mariano.

On the way back from the arena, his hand pressed over the new bandage, Cascales had shut his eyes. The men who had been waiting for him in his room knew when they saw him that the false words of the past years could no longer help: The bulls were bad. . . . The wind, no one could work in the wind, even Antonio Romero is afraid of the wind. . . . The crowds demand too much, you can't be your best every day. . . . The rain, it makes your feet slip. It had been the bulls, the crowd, the rain, the wind, the heat, the bad luck, never the man whose thigh aches.

"Was I good?" Cascales repeats.

"Today," Don Mariano answers, "you were good. But you tried too hard."

It had been bad luck. Cascales had drawn the worst bulls of the corrida. If Romero had faced the same bulls, he would have cut them into place, killed running far around the right horn, been insulted by the crowd, been paid extravagantly, and gone on the next day hoping for better bulls.

"You tried much too hard. Your bulls were bad,

especially the second one. You got what was good out of him, you worked well, made the faena. It was good; short but good. And then you started up again. Never prolong the faena beyond what the bull can take. Never."

Cascales knows that Don Mariano is correct in his criticism. "Yes, but I wanted to please. I wanted to give a good performance, one they'd remember."

"They'll remember eight good passes longer than fifty that don't work. The faena must be made with the bull, not for the public. Joselito always made a faena that fit his bull like a new suit."

Cascales wishes Joselito would not enter the conversation so often.

"Your first bull needed another pic. He came out too fast for the faena. You could have broken him with the cloth, but no, you insist on manoletinas. The bull was in no condition for them. With a bull like that, even Joselito would not have done what you tried."

"Sí, señor, the bull needed another pic, but they changed the suerte on me. He needed a pic farther front, to lose more blood and slow him up. The public understands nothing of the punishing, breaking passes. You understand, yes, but the public wants the feet together, and the manoletinas."

"Never mind the public,." Don Mariano answers. "Do what the bull needs. The bull commands until you learn to command the bull. You tried luck on a bad bull and hoped he would work out. It never does. A fine matador such as you knows this."

"Do you think the crowd liked me?" Cascales asks Don Mariano. "Do you think they want me back?"

"Of course they'd like to have you back," Don Mariano says.

This is what the matador craves to be the truth.

"Do you really think so?" the matador insists.

They would like to have you back, back at the café in Albacete—you were the greatest in Barcelona, but they'll have you back tomorrow, the manager thinks. He moves closer to the door and jiggles the change in his pocket.

"You were fine, matador. What I say is only meant to help you become better. We are from the same part of the country, aren't we?" Don Mariano places a hand on the matador's shoulder. Cascales is encouraged. The words feel good.

"Me voy—I'm going, matador," Don Mariano says.

The manager opens the door. *Why give him hope in words, what's the good? He'll only expect contracts next year, and next year I'm going to get somebody else. Julio Cascales is through.*

The telephone rings. The matador answers.

"Sí, sí, muy bien, I'm fine," the matador assures his mother. "No, it is nothing. I'm all right. I'm going to get Luis tonight at the sanatorium. We'll be home in the afternoon. Everything is fine. I promise. You'll see tomorrow. Yes, I was good. A friend here who saw Joselito thirty-eight times in one season says I was good. No, no, I didn't. I tried hard, but I didn't. The others, yes, they did, they had luck. Thank you. No, I'm not the best, but I tried. I'll get more contracts and we'll . . . no, no, NO! I won't! Don't ask me that. Please. Not any more. Not when things are better. When we have the farm, yes, I'll stop. Yes, and I'll make Luis stop. We'll talk tomorrow, not now. I'll be home. I have nothing to do tomorrow."

"Or any other day," the manager mutters.

Don Mariano stands still. He smiles at the manager, and while Cascales reassures his mother that a bull will not kill her sons, Don Mariano tells the manager of the money he loaned the impresarios of Valencia, and of Joselito.

It is 8:15 in the evening.

In front of the hotel, two cars are standing. They belong to Antonio Romero. The great rectangular Hispano is black. It is twenty-seven years old, and has transported the cuadrillas of many novilleros and matadors. At times, space has been found in the Hispano for the rising novillero who cannot afford a car of his own. The novillero has squeezed in with his men. Matadors who have had to sell their personal cars have returned to the same seat in the Hispano that they occupied on their way up. Twenty-eight men have lain seriously wounded in the car, and one has died on the back seat. No one remembers the death. It would be bad luck to know, and the car is good. It has traveled almost a million miles in Spain. It has taken men to more than 1,400 bullfights and has brought them back. When the car's owner has reached the top—and stayed there long enough—the car has been sold. Sometimes it has been sold when the owner stayed on his way up too long, or was killed, or quit.

In front of the Hispano, there is a dark-green latest-model Chrysler sedan from Detroit. Antonio Romero travels in this car alone with his driver. It is comfortable and spacious.

The lobby is filled: critics, impresarios, ranch owners, matadors, managers, photographers, sword handlers and aficionados are standing in shifting groups, talking. Antonio Romero is discussing with Manolo Ortega, two critics who are his friends, and Don Mariano the advantages a matador gains from placing his own banderillas.

Ortega turns to Romero. "You're lucky they don't know you're good with the sticks. Once you start you can't stop, and you have to be good every time. They yell if you don't do it, and they yell if you don't do it fabulously. They ask you why you don't let a man who is paid to do it, and who does it better than you, go out there and place them for you. Or else, when your faena is bad, they tell you you'd make a good banderillero for some novillero. It's good to put them in sometimes, but I often wish I'd never started."

"You can warm up the crowd for the faena with three great pairs better than anybody else," Don Mariano says.

"With your legs, it would be a shame if you didn't put in your own," one of the critics adds.

"You like it, Manolo, and it's good for you. Instead of sitting around in the *callejón,* smoking, or talking to the girls in the barrera, like Antonio, you get out there and earn your money like a man," the other critic, who is a friend of Antonio Romero's, says. The men laugh.

"Obviously I can't put in my own sticks," Romero says. "I'm too busy with the girls to do it, whereas the kid here, he'll be his own picador next year—won't need any cuadrilla. Maybe he'll get his older brother to be the bull."

"No, you, Antonio, you be the bull, and I'll have a girl in the cuadrilla—you'll charge all right and you won't get her, because she'll be mine." Manolo makes a gesture indicating the manner in which Antonio Romero will charge, and everyone laughs.

An aficionado friend of Don Mariano's joins the group. "What a disaster! Posada should quit," he says. "And he fights tomorrow." The friend has just spoken on the phone to an aficionado who has seen the Jiménez-Posada-Juan Ortega fight. "A disaster. He'll get killed if he gets near the bull, he's so scared, and if he doesn't, he'll really have to quit. No one's going to pay to see a man die of fear."

Manolo Ortega and Antonio Romero listen.

It can happen, Romero thinks. If I start to go down fast, I'll quit before I get that scared. I can make it now. If I only had the money I've made. Another two years and I'll be all right—if the next two years ever come to an end. Tomorrow's bulls are too far away for me to be afraid yet. The fear will start around noon tomorrow.

Antonio Romero's sword handler comes in through the revolving doors of the hotel, sees the matador and walks to his side. *"Señores,"* he greets the men. Antonio Romero nods. The sword handler leaves to pay the matador's bill at the reception desk and returns to the group of men.

"Everything is packed, matador."

"All right, let's go," Romero answers.

"Adiós." Romero turns to leave.

"Suerte," Don Mariano and his friend call after him. *"Suerte, hombre."*

"Gracias," Romero answers.

"See you," Romero says to Manolo Ortega.

"See you," Manolo answers

The revolving doors spin. Men wave to Antonio Romero. They want to speak to him, but the matador has already left.

A fine Atlantic mist covers the city. If a warm wind does not come up soon, the dwarfs, the clowns, the local boy and the crowd are going to be cold later on.

Antonio Romero's cuadrilla are stretching their legs before the trip. *Banderillero de confianza* José Vito, former matador, thirty-six years old, father of three sons, has the quickest eye and the best cape in the ring when someone is caught by the bull. Vito is laughing at a scene which is a part of the corner café.

Hop—hop—hop—hop—hop. A small dog jumps forward on his hind legs. Just as his nose reaches the shrimp held out to him by a customer sitting in the first row of tables on the sidewalk, the shrimp is raised a few inches too high for the dog to bite.

"Mire al perro, mire, look at the dog, look, look!" José Vito jumps up and down, imitating the dog's distress. "Look," he yells at the cuadrilla. "He has no front legs." And the dog falls painfully on its jaw.

Born with only two rear legs, the dog has proved to be the delight of the café's customers for years. Undoubtedly his presence has increased the café's income, a fact about which the café owner's wife never tires of informing her husband. He had wanted to drown the animal at birth, but she, out of kindness, nurtured the puppy and helped it to live its deformed existence. The dog is never beaten, and he gets a shrimp now and then and a daily meal, and beer on New Year's day, when he gets drunk and can't hop, and people buy beer and drink too much. The customers get thirsty laughing, and when the dog wakes up he is given a whole plate of shrimps for his pains.

Antonio Romero ignores José Vito, who is hopping like a maniac on the wet sidewalk. Vito has saved the matador's life too often for Antonio Romero to object to the banderillero's antics outside the ring.

The matador's driver holds the car door open. Antonio Romero jumps in, slams the thick door behind. It is warm inside. The radio is playing flamenco. Antonio watches the dog jump toward the shrimp and fall. *Pobrecito,* poor thing, he thinks, and smiles at the dog. The flamenco sings of a girl whose lover is dead. The driver, Pablo, settles into the front seat, The crowd, which has intently watched the matador enter his car, steps forward to look closer. The Chrysler leaves and the crowd turn their attention to the Hispano.

On top, the driver lashes down the tarpaulin which covers the baggage of ten men. In the Chrysler there is a *traje de luces* and four swords for the matador. In case the cuadrilla should fail to arrive, Antonio Romero can always appear using a makeshift cuadrilla gathered at the last moment. A wind blows the tarpaulin, making it difficult to handle.

"Let's go," the driver calls down, and seven men detach themselves from the crowd. They fill the car: three banderilleros, two picadors, sword handler, manager. The driver closes his door as the crowd moves closer. The men inside are jammed together: three on the rear seat, two on the extra seat built into the car, and three on the front seat. The least painful positions were found years ago.

"Wake us up for dinner, I'm hungry," one of the picadors says.

"Can't stop for long," the driver answers.

At the first red light José Vito and the manager close their eyes. The other men are talking, except for the hungry picador whose small eyes have given him the nickname "Ojitos." He has a headache.

It has been nine days since Antonio Romero and his men spent the night in bed. They have traveled 3,981 miles since a week ago Monday, when they appeared in Jerez de la Frontera. The schedule has been routine for a top matador during September.

9 Sept.	Monday		Jerez de la Frontera
		546 miles	
10 Sept.	Tuesday		Calatayud
		235 miles	
11 Sept.	Wednesday . . .		Albacete
		532 miles	
12 Sept.	Thursday . . .		La Coruña
		532 miles	
13 Sept.	Friday		Albacete
		288 miles	
14 Sept.	Saturday		Salamanca
		362 miles	
15 Sept.	Sunday		Huelva
		786 miles	
16 Sept.	Monday		Barcelona
		418 miles	
17 Sept.	Tuesday		Valladolid
		282 miles	
TODAY			
18 Sept.	Wednesday . . .		THE NORTH OF SPAIN
		650 miles	
TOMORROW			
19 Sept.	Thursday . . .		THE SOUTH OF SPAIN

Antonio Romero has been paid almost $50,000 during the past two weeks. His manager has retained one tenth legally. The cuadrilla has been paid $7,300. Legitimate expenses for food, lodg-

[TEXT CONTINUES ON PAGE 37.]

36A

ing and transportation have totaled $1,500. Advertising in *Dígame* and *El Ruedo* cost $400. The traditional bribes to the critics amount to almost $1,800. One third of the matador's income during this period has been spent.

Only $1,750 has been stolen from the remaining $34,000 by Antonio Romero's manager and sword handler. The matador is satisfied with this arrangement. His former manager stole everything he made in four successful seasons. In a world where payments are almost always made in cash and where legal documents rarely exist, it was easy to defraud the boy. The desire to become a matador, the fear of the bulls, and the fact that Antonio Romero now lived in luxury instead of the poverty into which he was born blinded him and made the theft possible. Antonio Romero became aware of his situation only when the manager tried to prove that he, the matador who had been robbed, owed the manager money. At present a sense of reality obliges him to demand proof of weekly deposits to his bank. The matador knows that he is still being cheated, but as long as it does not pass reasonable limits, he says nothing.

"We'll eat in Palencia," Romero says to his driver. "What time will we get there?"

"Before midnight, matador. There's some cheese and chicken if you are hungry."

The matador reaches into the box next to the bottle of mineral water, eats a piece of cheese, drinks, lights a cigarette and watches the white-painted trees flash by.

Pablo is bringing the Chrysler along the winding road from sea level up into the Cantabric mountains. It will not be possible to maintain high speeds until they reach the great plateau that will carry them south. The mountains are covered with trees. It is raining.

This is the nineteenth year Pablo has driven for a matador. He is one of the finest mechanics in Spain. Madrid garages could double his present salary if he preferred to fix the carburetors of the diplomatic corps rather than go to a bullfight every day with the matador who has faith in his driver. Pablo says to his wife and daughter, "When Antonio retires, I will cry. He is a son." Antonio will ask Pablo to drive for him when he retires, but Pablo will refuse. He will find another matador and go to the bullfights another year. His fear has never permitted him to face a bull.

The Chrysler's headlights illuminate the road. Antonio Romero is sleeping.

In the hotel lobby, Manolo Ortega is in the company of aficionados, men who have seen bulls die before Manolo Ortega's father was born, men who have seen and remember Bombita, Mazzantini, Guerrita. Manolo Ortega has amassed greater capital in a year and a half than some of his admirers have in a lifetime. The matador wears a yellow-and-green sports shirt which hangs outside his trousers. In his sword hand he carries a Donald Duck comic book and a brightly painted child's riding crop made of plastic. Manolo Ortega, matador de toros, is switching the pants cuffs of the elderly aficionados with his toy. Among the men to whom the matador is talking are the architect who built the Madrid subway, an eye surgeon from Barcelona, a writer from Peru and three business men whose names appear on their products throughout the world.

In a corner of the lobby, the local impresarios are conversing with Manolo Ortega's manager. The three men are pleased. It is certain that Manolo Ortega will return for at least two bullfights in this city during next year's feria. At noon the impresarios paid in cash the sum agreed upon for this afternoon's appearance. Manolo's manager shakes hands with the impresarios and walks away.

"Time to go, Manolo," the manager says to the boy.

"Is the car here, Don Fernando?"

"Yes, it's waiting. Come on."

The group of aficionados begins to dissolve and join other groups in the lobby. Switching his own trouser leg, Manolo Ortega walks out of the hotel.

The cold mist is rising. The crowd in front of the hotel has grown. Ten minutes ago, Manolo Ortega's cuadrilla left directly from their hotel. The crowd watches the brightly lit chandeliers swirl into stars as Manolo Ortega revolves through the doors.

A dark-blue convertible Mercedes-Benz sedan is waiting. It is the matador's personal car, which he has owned for six weeks. Until the Mercedes could be bought, Manolo Ortega rode with his cuadrilla.

A boy only six years younger than Manolo Ortega stands next to the Mercedes, feeling the steel curve of the front fender. He is hiding a pair of bull's horns under a wet newspaper held in his left arm. The Englishman who bought the horns from the butcher at the Plaza de Toros carelessly placed his trophies on the sidewalk next to his chair while he drank a beer at a café; he will not be able to impress his friends in London. Now the boy will be able to attend classes at the bullfight school; his older brother will permit him. His brother is at home in the kitchen, afraid of the yearling bull he will face in a few hours.

Manolo Ortega's driver turns on the radio, and the matador listens to a New Orleans jazz program being broadcast by A.F.N Munich.

In the Chrysler, Antonio Romero is resting. Pablo is passing an oxcart on a curve.

In the Hispano Vito has awakened and is thinking about his wife in Sevilla. She will have a child tomorrow, the doctor has said. "Ojitos" is eating a sandwich.

"Lay off," Vito says to him. "You're already half as big as one of your horses." And he slaps the picador on his large stomach.

The picador still has a headache. The fourth bull charged suddenly while he was momentarily off balance. The bull attacked the fallen man, who lay on the ground, his head pinned between the horse and the barrera. The surgeon stood up. Vito made the *quite*, taking the bull away with his cape, before the matadors reached the picador. He had started in before "Ojitos" had even hit the sand. The surgeon sat down and said to his assistant, "He's got the best eye around."

The Hispano is not far behind the Chrysler. The cars must still travel over seven hundred miles. It is nine o'clock.

Across Spain the cafés are full. The sharp concentration that was focused on the bull ring has been scattered. The streets, which were empty under the violent sun during the day, are crowded. The children are playing in the parks. Men and women, coming from nowhere, are spending the first hours of the night strolling, talking, meeting friends by chance, sitting at a café because there is an empty table, buying the papers as they pass a newsstand. Plans are made and forgotten, drinks are ordered and canceled, hours are spent righting the world. Everyone is talking: of wedding rings and revolutions, of beaches and water, of friends and farming and work and of the day and of tomorrow.

At first those who have been to the bullfights speak only of the bulls. They have seen the bulls challenged and they have seen them die. The matadors are spoken of in direct relation to the bulls.

There is no aspect of the bullfight which does not interest the aficionado. Endless discussions are held in which opinions exist as evidence of the truth. Facts are denied and supported according to the verdict given by the individual. It is affirmed that the bullfight needs the sun, and yet someone says that the best bullfights are often seen in the rain. It is argued whether or not a heavy man will suffer a worse wound on the horn than a small man. The sand in the Sevilla bull ring is the most beautiful in Spain. There are men who prefer Pamplona, and there are men who become involved in the complex history of a single pass, or the evolution of the pic, the banderilla, the muleta.

The talk is everywhere, in the homes, on the streets, in the villages and cities, in trains and in cars.

There are wealthy aficionados who are driven by their chauffeurs, and men who walk miles in the sun and dust. The intellectual, the farmer, the doorman, the pilot, the banker bring their opinions to the bullfight. At night, when the men who have fought during the day travel across Spain, the bullfight finds itself in the aficionados.

The talk is interminable.

FOUR

JUAN ORTEGA is driving south. He has left the city in the east where he appeared this afternoon with Francisco Jiménez and Emilio Posada. By 10:30 tonight he will reach the southern city toward which his younger brother Manolo and Antonio Romero are traveling.

Emilio Posada has decided to eat in his room. He would enjoy a Coca-Cola in the lobby or in a café. A drive outside the city would ease the pain, but his driver has just called to say that the car is in the garage. The generator is broken. Posada is focusing his attention on his foot, the one the bull stepped on.

After I eat, I'll go to the Virgin. I don't care how they stare, or what they say, I'll go to the Virgin. Across the lobby, quickly, it's not a big lobby, and in the taxi nobody can see me. In church no one will do anything. I'll be safe in the church. I'll give the Virgin something. I'll promise the Virgin. Tomorrow the bulls will charge. There will be four bad bulls and two easy ones, and I'll get the two easy ones. If I promise the Virgin, I'll get the easy ones. If I promise and give her something also, I'll be sure to get the two easy bulls, and tomorrow I'll be good, better than I was when I was the best, better than before the wound, and I'll be on top again and have contracts and my own car back, and Maria Luisa. The Virgin can make the bulls easy, she can, she can, somebody has to, Santa Virgen, Santa, Santa Virgen, *ayúdame*, help me, help. The pain in the matador's foot has stopped. I promise, make it easy, please, I promise, please, I promise to . . . The waiter with the dinner for Emilio Posada interrupts the supplication.

Downstairs, Francisco Jiménez is standing in the lobby with Carlos Huerta, matador de toros. Huerta is thirty-nine years old. He has made an excellent income from his profession for twenty years. He is married and has three daughters. Two of his brothers are matadors, one brother and two first cousins are novilleros, three are banderilleros, one uncle is a picador, and one a manager. Huerta's father owns a bull ring in an important city. Carlos Huerta has recently bought a ranch on which he will live and breed bulls when he retires. He has been wounded many times, before he was married and since. He has the stability of a man who works well. He has never been a phenomenon. It has never been said that he is better than Joselito or Belmonte, yet he is honest, a fine matador. He performs no stunts before the public. He kills excellently. Carlos Huerta is confident and he gives a sense of order to the bullfights in which he appears.

Tonight at eleven o'clock he is going to the Carmen Montoya show with Francisco Jiménez. Tomorrow he will appear in this city with Emilio Posada and a third matador who has not as yet been chosen.

Domingo Vasquez, who is in the hospital in Barcelona, had been announced earlier. His wound forced the impresario to find someone to replace him. The matador who was picked twisted his knee badly in Salamanca today, and cannot walk. Cascales is of course available, but he cannot be put on the same cartel as Posada. The impresario is telephoning. During the last hour and a half he has spoken twice with Madrid, once with Salamanca, and three times with San Sebastián, where he is also the impresario. One of the matadors who was to appear in tomorrow's bullfight in San Sebastián was seriously wounded this afternoon in Salamanca. The impresario has canceled the San Sebastián bullfight. No proper alternate can be found.

The second matador who was to appear in San Sebastián tomorrow is on his way from Africa to Madrid by plane. This afternoon he fought in Oran.

The car is waiting in Madrid to take him to San Sebastián. The impresario is giving a message to an official at the Madrid airport.

"I will board the plane personally," the official answers. "Yes. Yes. It is certain. Yes, yes, I will. I will inform the matador myself," the official assures the impresario. "San Sebastián is canceled. You will find a cuadrilla if his men cannot arrive in time. He is to leave directly for the Huerta-Posada fight. Glad to help." At home tonight the official will enjoy telling this story.

The impresario leaves the telephone booth. As he passes Jiménez and Huerta in the lobby, he gives them the news for tomorrow.

"Bad luck about San Sebastián, Don Manuel. Couldn't you find anybody?" Huerta asks.

"Nobody that can draw a crowd, except Juan Ortega. He's not fighting tomorrow. It's not so bad, though. In the north it's cold, and the money has gone back to Madrid. If I could have put you two up there we could have drawn them down from Biarritz."

The impresario joins Don Alipio Pérez and his *mayoral* at the other end of the lobby. Both men are wearing soft riding boots. Don Alipio's are hidden under a carefully tailored suit. The *mayoral* is not used to comfortable lobbies. His life is spent on a horse, directing the management of his employer's ranch. He stands with dignity beside Don Alipio, awaiting orders.

The impresario discusses the purchase of three corridas from Don Alipio for next year. The *mayoral* supplies the detailed information which Don Alipio does not have immediately available. They discuss dates, and Don Alipio gives his word to supply the corridas the impresario has requested.

Carlos Huerta turns to ask the concierge a question, leaving Francisco Jiménez standing alone for an instant. Immediately Jiménez is approached and enclosed by a group of men, men who do not hesitate to put an arm around the matador's shoulders, men who are disinterested in each other and who are only brought together in a common desire to seem intimate friends of the famous matador. Francisco Jiménez stands quietly in their midst and becomes an object on display. Jokes are offered as bait in the hope that the matador will laugh. In an attempt to seduce, each man acts in a familiar and tempting manner. Cigars are given to the matador, and matches are burned in his face to light them. If the matador speaks, his words are saved, to be enlarged upon later and retold as having been uttered in confidence to the individual.

A photographer raises his camera. The men in the group struggle, each trying to stand as close as possible to the matador. The group smiles, staring at the lens. Carlos Huerta turns around, takes Francisco Jiménez by the arm, and the two matadors walk into the dining room.

The men shift their attention to the photographer, ask for his address, hand him their cards, and try to find out when the prints will be ready. For a moment the men remain together, extolling Francisco Jiménez to one other, and then they separate.

The matadors order their dinner. The menu is long, and Jiménez does not feel like choosing. He accepts the first suggestions made by the headwaiter and reaches for a roll, but decides to wait. He stares at the twisted napkin on his plate.

At the next table four ranch owners are eating. Jiménez and Huerta have killed bulls bred by each of the four men. At another table, three critics are having a drink with Jiménez' manager. The room is filled with men who have been to the bullfight. A friend of Francisco Jiménez' looks around, sees the matador, and joins him. Jiménez stands, calls the headwaiter over and helps his friend to order. He tells a joke, and the friend laughs. Jiménez offers him a drink and shows him the supply of cigars he has collected in the lobby.

"They're all for you and Carlos. You know I don't smoke."

He shrugs his shoulders, smiles and pulls his chair up closer to the table. The expression of melancholy on his face is gone. He tells a ridiculous and involved story of the day the motor on his boat exploded and covered with oil some government officials he had taken for a ride. Francisco Jiménez pours the wine. He invites his friend to the show he and Huerta are going to see later on. The three men toast each other.

FIVE

IN THE NORTH, the impresarios are arguing with Julio Cascales' manager.

"We will not pay more."

"The Plaza was not full. Take thirty-five and be glad for it. We will not pay another peseta."

One of the impresarios is small, totally bald, and, as always, dressed in black. His partner is stout, smiling. For many years both men were horse contractors. Through the misfortunes of the men with whom the impresarios associate, the two ex-horse contractors have risen to a strong position. Fraud and theft have given them control of four important bull rings. They are hated by the matadors.

"We will pay thirty-five."

"Fifty—that's your idea, not ours. We pay thirty-five for Cascales. Go ask him which he prefers, thirty-five or nothing."

The two impresarios turn to leave.

"You said fifty," Cascales' manager argues. "You said you'd pay fifty thousand pesetas for him. He was paid eighty thousand in Barcelona, and now you want to pay thirty-five. You said fifty on the phone."

Long ago, the two men who are cheating Cascales were nicknamed "Los Monos"—the monkeys—by the impresario in Barcelona. The nickname stuck.

On the telephone, Cascales' manager had been promised fifty thousand pesetas. If Domingo Vasquez had been able to fill his contract, Los Monos would have had to pay him 150,000. Cascales can do nothing. If he tries to protect himself, the impresarios will pay him the fifteen thousand they are stealing, but Cascales will never again replace a wounded matador in one of their bull rings.

Los Monos are aware that Cascales prefers a fight for thirty-five thousand to one for nothing and Cascales' manager is also aware of this fact when he accepts their offer. To the manager, the difference is small; his tenth of the theft is only fifteen hundred pesetas. If he gets a good novillero to manage next year he'll need Los Monos to get him started. Why make trouble for fifteen hundred pesetas for a matador who's through?

Next year Los Monos will be certain to telephone Cascales whenever they need a replacement. They will offer thirty thousand. Cascales will accept. They will pay twenty. Cascales will no longer have a manager and will accept the twenty. The following year the possible theft will be too small for Los Monos to bother telephoning Cascales. There will be other matadors going down who will have better cartel. They can be offered seventy-five thousand and cheated out of at least a third of the offer. They, too, will not make trouble—will not be able to make trouble. They will need the money. If Posada is not killed, and if he has a good fight, people will come to see him again, and he will fight for very little and can be cheated out of a great deal.

Los Monos paid Antonio Romero's manager 190, 000 pesetas, and Manolo Ortega's sword handler 150,000 at noon. It is unfortunate to pay such large sums, Los Monos think, but you have to when a man has cartel, because you need him more than he needs you. Maybe Manolo Ortega will be wounded and become afraid; then Los Monos can catch him on the way down.

Having stolen a small sum of money, Los Monos leave the hotel lobby. They ride home in their American cars.

Until his son became a matador, Julio Cascales' father worked ten hours a day, six days a week, for more than a year, in order to earn fifteen thousand pesetas. He worked for twenty-six years repairing roads with his hands, before his eldest son became the object of fraud. After expenses, Julio Cascales will return home with a profit equal to a year's work on the roads. He will have earned this amount by exposing his body to the horns for twenty minutes. The public prefers Francisco Jiménez. This enables Jiménez in a week to earn the equivalent of two hundred years of work on the road. A neighbor of Julio Cascales', who was born lucky, a boy only four years older than Cascales, who is now retired, earned enough from the bulls to be able to spend over a thousand dollars a day for two years. Broke, he returned to the bulls and earned a second fortune, which he kept.

At 9:15, Julio Cascales is speaking with Don Mariano Martín in the lobby. His manager has not told him of the theft.

"Señor Julio Cascales. Señor Julio Cascales," a page boy calls out. *"Teléfono para el Señor Cascales."* The boy is ten years old. He has been working for nine hours. He helps his father to support the family. It is necessary to do this in order to eat.

Don Mariano gestures at the boy. "Here's the matador," he calls out. The boy joins the two men.

"Telephone for Señor Cascales."

Cascales follows the boy the length of the lobby, through many groups of aficionados. No one speaks to him.

The call is from Julio Cascales' younger brother Luis at the Sanatorio de Toreros in Madrid. Luis Cascales is a novillero. Three weeks ago he was gored in the right armpit. Luis had been unaware that his bull was gaining ground on him in a series of four tight verónicas. On the fourth pass he had hesitated to complete the series by quickly drawing the cape into his hip in a media verónica, and so permit the bull to exit from the encounter. The novillero had hoped to do a fourth and a fifth and a sixth verónica, if possible. The more he could do and the better he could do, the quicker he would have more contracts. The bull's mass had carried him by the boy's extended cape three times. Three times the bull had passed him. Three times luck and the initial power of the bull had made the boy look good. At no time did the boy command the bull to pass. The bull was good. He didn't hook; let him pass as often as possible, as close as possible. That's all that is needed for contracts: many passes, many close passes. The crowd seemed to enjoy watching the bull run in front of the boy. They were shrieking *"Olé!"* What else was needed for contracts? *Olés* and the ears he would get on this easy bull, this bull that was doing the work, of which the boy was ignorant. A man in the *callejón* whispered, "He'll get it," and the boy was caught on the fourth pass, because he was wrong, and the bull was right. He could have made a fourth pass if he had been able to dominate the bull. He had stood still. He had swung his cape gracefully and in accord with the bull's charge, but he had not forced the bull to his will. He had been unable to do so, and he was gored by the left horn, through the muscles of his shoulder and upper arm.

"How do you feel?" Julio Cascales asks his brother.

"Fine."

"You can leave tonight, can't you?"

"Yes, and I want to get out."

"Good. I'll come by and pick you up. We'll drive straight home."

"How'd it go?" Luis asks.

"Fine, fine. I'll tell you about it. I don't know what time we'll get in, so you might as well go to bed. *Adiós*. See you later, Luis."

"*Adiós*, Julio." Now that he is going home, Luis Cascales hopes his manager has some contracts ready.

SIX

IN THE SOUTH of Spain, Juan Ortega is eating a large dinner and joking with his friends and the waiter. Tomorrow he will not face two bulls.

The bull ring is near the hotel where Juan Ortega is eating. The stands are beginning to fill. Along the edge of the barrera six heavy crates are standing next to one another. In each crate there is a Conde de la Corte bull. These are the bulls for tomorrow, the first corrida of the feria. For weeks, throughout the city, posters have been announcing the time, the place, the prices, the bulls, the men: ANTONIO ROMERO—FRANCISCO JIMÉNEZ—MANOLO ORTEGA.

At eight o'clock this morning a truck left the Conde de la Corte ranch near Badajoz. At dawn the *mayoral* had supervised the crating of the bulls. At each end of the crate there is a sliding door which can be pulled upward by a man standing on top. The six crates were placed end to end to form a tunnel, one end of which faced an exit to the corral where the bulls had spent the night. When the *mayoral* gave the signal to start loading, all crate doors were opened, except the last in the row. The gate to the corral opened. A bull rushed out into the tunnel, ran the length of the six crates, and stopped before the closed door at the end. The door behind slammed down. One. In ten minutes the other five bulls were loaded in a similar manner. The six crates were hoisted onto the truck. Water and food were placed in each crate.

On the trip, wherever the truck had stopped, a crowd gathered. Men crossed the street, leaving their drinks on the tables of the cafés. Children stopped their games and women paused on their way to market. The crowd stared at the six crates, their eyes eagerly searching the narrow air slots, hoping to see the tip of a horn or a black muzzle.

This evening the truck drove through the city into the bull ring. "The bulls." Conversations were changed. "Bulls." Opinions were given. "Bulls, bulls, bulls." As the truck passed, the word was repeated in the cafés, along the streets, "Bulls." The crowd expanded into the city.

In the arena itself, at nine o'clock, the crates were slid onto the sand from the truck. At eleven o'clock tonight they will be opened, and the crowd will see the Conde de la Corte bulls.

In the east, Francisco Jiménez is sitting in the lobby of his hotel, surrounded by five girls. The matador is listening. One of the girls is extremely attractive and attempts to be friendly with Jiménez. He makes no response; instead he shows off a silver statue of the Virgin, which a friend has given him. The girls ask him how he dared to kneel in front of the bull this afternoon. The matador smiles quickly and orders a Coca-Cola from the waiter.

Francisco Jiménez is waiting for Carlos Huerta. The show the two matadors are going to see starts at eleven o'clock. Jiménez' driver is ready with the matador's Cadillac at the front door. A crowd is standing around the car.

Upstairs, Emilo Posada is alone in his room. He has finished eating, and his foot occupies his attention. The matador wants to visit the Virgin and promise her that he will be good if she makes the bulls easy. He stands up to go.

Antonio Romero is awake. Pablo tunes the radio to the station that will give a report on the afternoon's bullfights at eleven o'clock.

Manolo Ortega has fallen asleep, still holding his toy riding crop. His driver has thrown a blanket over the matador.

It is 10:40.

In the north, an inland wind has swept the cold mist toward the ocean. The local boy has left his mother's kitchen, where he sat all evening. His younger brother is cleaning the horns he stole from the Englishman. The local boy wears a rented *traje de luces* which is too tight. He has spent all the money he earned during the past four months in order to have the opportunity to kill a yearling bull in front of the crowd tonight. He worked eleven hours a day to earn this money. His name is Ramón Quintana, and he is sixteen years old. It is possible that in a few years this boy will earn a quarter of a million dollars in a six-month period. It is probable that he will earn less. It is unlikely that he will be dead.

Since Ramón Quintana was five years old, he has wanted to become a matador.

Last year a French magazine reporter visited the bullfight school where Ramón Quintana has been training. He asked Ramón a question. Ramón answered, "No, it is not for the money, not for the money alone. It is so that when I walk in the street, they will say, 'There is Ramón Quintana,' or, when I sit in a café, the waiter will say, 'That is Ramón Quintana.' It is so that the newspapers and the magazines will write about Ramón Quintana and the radio will speak of Ramón Quintana."

It is 10:42. The *paseo* will take place in eighteen minutes. The band, the dwarfs, the clowns are ready and leaving the hotel for the bull ring. The stands are already three quarters full. Underneath the stands, four yearling bulls are waiting. The crowd of women and children is cheerful and eager. The sign *"No hay billetes"*—No tickets—was hung outside the ticket booths at 9:30. The impresarios are satisfied.

Ramón Quintana prays before a gilt statue of the Virgin in his bedroom. Tonight he will kill for the first time. His younger brother watches him from the doorway. The boy's father is on the sidewalk waiting for the taxi to take his son to the bull ring to kill a yearling bull in front of 15,000 people. Ramón's mother is not at home. She is sitting with her sister, crying. Ramón's mother is praying to the Virgin.

Ramón Quintana, *becerrista,* is standing straight before the image of the Virgin. Ramón's friends are in the hall. A taxi turns the corner of the street. Ramón's father runs into the courtyard and shouts through the laundry up to the fourth floor, *"Está aquí"*—It's here. In the taxi, two men, both over forty, are waiting. Each is wearing an old *traje de luces.* One of these men is a newspaper vendor, the other a bus conductor. Since they were young, these men have been fifth-rate banderilleros. The boy is paying the men five dollars each for the effort they will make.

It is 10:44. Ramón stops praying. His younger brother kisses him and whispers, *"Suerte."*

"Gracias," Ramón answers, *"gracias."*

As Ramón walks downstairs, the friends, the neighbors wait for him on each floor.

"Suerte, Ramón."

"Suerte."

"Suerte."

On each floor Ramón hears the word *"Suerte."*

"Suerte" follows him through the courtyard, meets him on the sidewalk where the neighbors from next door and across the street are waiting. The butcher, the shoe-repair man, the grocer, the waiter from the café, the bootblack and the garage mechanic are looking on. *"Suerte, Suerte, Suerte."* The women watch. Young boys shout, then become quiet.

"Suerte." The single word is interrupted by the blind woman who sells national lottery tickets in the neighborhood. *"Hay billetes, hay billetes,* tickets, tickets, seven million, *siete millones, siete millones, siete, siete, siete,* luck with me. *Siete Millones, millones, millones, millones, hay billetes,* seven million, seven, *hay, hay!"* Her chant pierces the crowd.

Ramón is followed into the taxi by his father and brother. The taxi starts. Hands reach in to touch the *becerrista* Ramón Quintana. The *paseo* is at eleven o'clock.

It is 10:47.

A large car containing the eight dwarfs passes in front of the hotel where Julio Cascales is eating. Another car follows with the four comics. The men inside the hotel, the men concerned with the formal bullfight, ignore the dwarfs and the comics.

In a narrow street, the dwarfs are delayed by a crowd which is looking at the dismembered carcasses of the six bulls which were killed during the late afternoon. The meat, hanging in the windows of a butcher shop, is for sale. On the sign above the shop, in yellow letters, are written the names of the two men who stole from Julio Cascales this evening.

At 10:55, Ramón Quintana is standing underneath the bull ring, an empty circle of sand in front of him. The two banderilleros are helping the boy place his *capote de paseo* correctly over the left shoulder, around the back, and under the right arm. Ramón Quintana practiced at home this afternoon, but now the *capote de paseo* keeps slipping. The *traje de luces* he is wearing is pink, faded and repaired. The hard gold embroidery is tarnished and gone in spots. The red silk roses embroidered on it are frayed. Ramón's father is in the *callejón*, unpacking the capotes and muletas. The swords are in their case leaning against the foot of the stands. The arena is brightly lit.

Ramón Quintana is a minor attraction whose presence is ignored by the majority. The crowd has come to see the dwarfs and the comics. The adult dwarfs are dressed as infant sailors, their short twisted legs stuffed into white trousers, their thick torsos covered in dark-blue sweaters. On their enlarged heads they wear white caps. The four comics represent a fat fireman, a scrawny bellboy, a dandy in evening clothes, and a nervous redheaded woman with a single huge breast under a red sweater.

There are far fewer men in the stands than there were this afternoon. The children are excited, impatient, loud. Their mothers are glad to be out of the house.

The procession forms—dwarfs, comics, brass band, Ramón Quintana. The boy crosses himself, and the band plays.

It is eleven o'clock.

SEVEN

THE NIGHT SKY is clear over Spain.

The curtain goes up. Francisco Jiménez and Carlos Huerta are sitting together in the third row. To the right of the matadors, in a box, the picadors from their cuadrillas are applauding the girls on the stage.

Across the square from the theater, Emilio Posada has reached the cathedral. He is praying to the Virgin. There is no wind in the east. It is hot.

In the north the dwarfs waddle and tumble across the sand. Ramón Quintana bows to the President.

Antonio Romero, in the Chrysler, listens to the critic on the radio.

José Vito, "Ojitos" and the cuadrilla have stopped to eat. The driver is filling the Hispano with gas.

Manolo Ortega is sleeping on the back seat of his new Mercedes. The matador's toy riding crop has fallen to the floor.

In the city toward which the cars are traveling, Juan Ortega has gone bowling with friends. The night is warm in the south. In the bull ring, the crowd is anxious to see the Conde de la Corte bulls. The aficionados are waiting. In the stands and in the cafés they are giving their opinions. The matadors are acclaimed and denounced. The bulls are discussed, their bravery questioned and confirmed. Opinions are divided.

Tomorrow, at 5:30 in the afternoon the first bullfight of the feria will begin.

Ramón Quintana enters the *callejón*. Ramón and his cuadrilla throw their *capotes de paseo* to friends at the barrera. They stand quietly while the crowd laughs at the dwarfs, who have formed a pyramid in the center of the ring. The pyramid collapses, and the fat fireman becomes violently angry. He kicks at the pile of wriggling dwarfs. In mock agony, the small men tumble and roll on the sand. The spectacle of eight men with distorted bodies being kicked is amusing to the crowd. A vicious blow is aimed at the bulging forehead of a dwarf lying inert on the sand, and, as his seven companions mournfully carry his lifeless body from the arena, and as the fat fireman victoriously mocks the bowlegs of the dwarfs by imitating their grotesque movements, the first number of the evening comes to a close.

A few children are deceived by the simulated death and begin to cry. Their pain is relieved by the return of all eight dwarfs, who suddenly appear to take a bow. Mothers explain that it is all in fun and that no one is really dead.

At 11:15, in the south, the bull ring is full. The crowd is quiet as the *mayoral* from the Conde de la Corte ranch and two assistants walk across the sand. The *toril* gate is opened and five huge, wide-horned oxen enter. The bulls will be less nervous if the ring is not empty. The *mayoral* and his men climb on top of the crates. Thick metal bolts and chains are released. The oxen move without purpose. The *mayoral* pulls at the door of the first crate. It sticks. The attention of the crowd is sharply directed. An assistant pulls with the *mayoral*. The door jolts open.

Slowly the bull puts his head out and instantly charges into the center of the ring. The oxen scatter. The bull's head is high, the eyes are alert, the immense muscles relaxed. The bull runs, stops, turns.

The bull is five years old, in possession of courage and intelligence, capable of intense rage and blind attack, able to learn from experience and calculate his defense. He weighs 1,185 pounds. He fights with great strength, speed and accuracy. He discharges an attack instantly, in silence and with precision. The crowd senses the power beneath the black hide. It applauds the bull.

The *mayoral* is ready to open the second crate. Suddenly the crate moves. The men on top lose their balance and grab onto the edges. The crowd imagines the bull inside and, as the bull's fury shakes the massive crate, their expectation grows. The position of the *mayoral* and his men is dangerous. They jump onto the empty crate beside them as the first bull charges from the center of the ring.

From the crowd a young boy leaps into the *callejón* and runs onto the sand toward the bull. He holds a torn muleta in one hand. The bull charges. The crowd shrieks in open horror. For a moment the oxen distract the bull's charge. The *mayoral* and his men jump to the sand, and while the *mayoral* runs at the boy, his men incite the bull to charge.

The boy is frantic. For weeks he has forced himself toward this moment. An insane desire to succeed has overcome his fear. The *mayoral* grabs at the boy. The boy races after the bull, seeking the triumph which only the bull can give him. The bull charges at the men instead. The *mayoral* catches the boy, throws him to the ground, tears the muleta from his hand and shoves him toward the police in the *callejón*. The boy is led to jail. The crowd is angry at the boy. If he had worked with the muleta, the authorities would have had to send the bull to the slaughterhouse tonight. The crowd applauds the courage of the *mayoral* and the men. They have saved the bull.

The second bull is released. The bull looks up, turns and jabs quickly at one of the crates. Six hundred pounds of wood and metal are jolted a foot into the air.

The fifth bull is larger than the others. On his flank the brand number is clearly visible in the electric light: 11. He throws one of the oxen to the ground, exciting the crowd. The bulls stand together in a herd. The last bull is released.

Number 11 attacks. The bulls lock horns. The *mayoral* becomes afraid. A year ago Number 11 killed a bull on the ranch. The bulls fight. Number 11 backs away, jabs, turns, shifts, throws his opponent and trots away. The fallen bull hooks the bull nearest him. The *toril* gate is opened and tomorrow's corrida follows the oxen into the corral behind the bull ring.

In the north, a fanfare of trumpets sounds.

A very small yearling bull rushes from the dark *toril* into the brightly lit arena. The children in the stands screech in delight.

The four comics dash at the bull, waving their capes in unison. The yearling charges. The men pretend to be struck with an insane fear. They run to hide behind one another, trembling in terror. The yearling is confused, and the crowd laughs.

A series of absurd and clever stunts demanding remarkable skill and knowledge follow, until the bull becomes an object of total ridicule. The acrobatic bellboy plays the hero who protects the redheaded lady with the single huge breast. The yearling charges. The bellboy panics, and the lady grabs the animal's tail and pulls. Wriggling under the inept horns, the bellboy wraps his legs around the bull's neck. The small animal becomes powerless, and the crowd laughs. The yearling struggles and kicks. The band is playing. The redheaded lady falls, loses her breast, which bounces across the sand, and the fat fireman runs screaming into the arms of the dandy in evening clothes. The two men dance together. The yearling charges. Holding each other at arm's length, the couple separates, the precise second that the bull rushes between them. They instantly reunite in a musical embrace. Stalking the small animal as if it were a tiger, the dandy ridicules his own fear. Bewildered, the bull adds to its own absurdity.

The dandy then lies on the sand reading a newspaper he has pulled from his pocket, his padded bottom in the air. The yearling attempts to gore. The dandy offers his bottom and accepts the charge. He continues to read, ignoring the horns. The yearling runs away and is forced to charge by the bellboy. When the bull is a yard from the man's body, the bellboy leaps into the air, his legs spread wide apart, and, as the animal passes beneath him, he jabs in the steel-barbed banderillas. The animal jumps in pain, and the bellboy takes a bow.

The dandy, the redheaded lady and the bellboy form a semicircle around the fat fireman as he profiles with the sword and goes in to kill. Three feet of curved steel pierce the dazed animal. His body quivers from the shock.

The four comedians quiver in mock sympathy. The crowd roars. The animal wavers on its legs, dying. The comedians waver. One of the yearling's forelegs gives way. The comedians fall to one knee. The bull falls on its muzzle; its nostrils fill with sand. The comedians put their hands down and wave their bottoms. The crowd laughs. The bull's body collapses. The comedians drop in false death. The bull tries to get up and falls again. The men try, too, and fall again. The bull shudders in death. The men shudder. The crowd laughs. The bull's legs twitch and it dies. The men twitch their limbs, lie still on their backs for an instant, and stand up to receive the applause. The body is dragged from the arena as the band breaks into a pompous military march. The dwarfs tumble. The band marches, and the bellboy changes into a mad scientist wielding a four-foot knife. He transforms three of the dwarfs into a single three-headed monster which rolls out of the ring.

Ramón Quintana is next.

The boy crosses himself as the yearling bull runs onto the sand. The bull is skinny and fast. His horns are six inches long and thin. The horns Ramón's brother brought home this evening are twenty inches long, and thick.

The crowd is quiet.

Ramón Quintana steps through the *burladero* and faces a bull before a crowd for the first time. The small salary earned during the months of hard work has been put into the next ten minutes.

Three verónicas begin to assure the crowd that Ramón Quintana has an idea of what he is doing. The first two are slow and give an impression of control. The third is too fast; the bull does not follow, and Ramón is forced to pull his legs back quickly to avoid the horns. Instantly the bull turns and charges. The boy has lost his ground, and is unprepared. The yearling chases him to the barrera and the crowd laughs. Ramón's younger brother is angry and afraid. One of the banderilleros runs in with his cape and draws the bull away from Ramón.

The time on the bull-ring clock is 12:30.

Ramon drops to his knees. I should have done a larga when he came out and then the verónicas. His thoughts do not have time to focus. The yearling bull charges. Ramón's cape lies before him on the sand, slightly to his right. Ramón flings the cloth quickly over his left shoulder into the air. The horns follow the cloth. A second pass brings cheers from the public. On his feet, reassured, Ramón attempts a series of more difficult passes. He succeeds in gaining the public's approval by demonstrating that he wants to please. His tentative knowledge of the bulls, and luck, keep him from being wounded. The bull is good. He charges straight and has good eyes.

The trumpets blow. Ramón waits by the barrera. The two banderilleros do their work safely and ineptly. Ramón steps out and gestures toward the President, signifying he wishes the suerte changed. The crowd applauds the gesture, thinking that he sincerely wishes his bull to be in a lively condition for the faena. Ramón is motivated by the fact that he has seen Francisco Jiménez do the same thing; after having instructed his picadors practically to kill his bull, Jiménez has gained the crowd's favor by requesting that the bull be spared the third pair of banderillas.

Ramón's father hands his son the muleta and sword. Ramón bows to the President and asks permission to kill the yearling bull. The crowd is expectant. The boy is better than the usual local. He steps to the center of the ring, removes his montera and dedicates the death of his first bull to the public. The crowd applauds.

Quietly Ramón Quintana approaches the bull. He is confident. The animal backs away, paws the ground in cowardice. He was good a moment ago. If he is going to start this, I can't do anything. . . . The boy is afraid, not of the horns now but of failure, and of the futility of the months of work. If I can only do a good faena with him. I can do it! Ramón approaches the bull, offers him the muleta in his left hand. The bull backs away. Ramón has a picture in his mind of the bull's backing away forever. He shakes the muleta and hits it with the sword. The boy's father and brother are motionless. He shakes the muleta again. The bull backs away. Whistles are heard from the crowd. Ramón is hurt. It is not my fault, he wants to tell everybody, it is not, I am trying, but the bull just doesn't charge. I'll rush in, step aside, and give the bull the muleta as he charges. I'll give him my body and change him to the cloth. I'll *make* him charge.

The bull charges before the boy is set. Instinctively Ramón flings the cloth in front of him as protection. This insane action draws the bull directly into the defenseless boy. He is hit and thrown backward by the bull's charge.

The muleta hides the possible existence of a wound from the crowd. The banderilleros make the *quite*, and Ramón stands up, holding both hands to his groin. One of the banderilleros helps the boy to the *callejón*. A moment passes as the crowd whispers.

Ramón straightens his bent body. He pushes his father's hands away and walks back onto the sand. He gestures the banderilleros away from the bull. "Get out, *fuera, fuera*, get out, get out!" he shrieks, and the two middle-aged men go slowly to the barrera. The crowd whispers, "Nothing, nothing, nothing, he's all right," and applauds.

The boy is angry. His fear of failure, his fear of the horns have become anger, anger at the small bull. During the largas Ramón had liked the bull. He had liked him very much. They had worked together, and the crowd had enjoyed the work.

"I'll force you to charge." He gives the young bull five left-hand natural passes. One, silence. Two, silence. Three, *Olé*. Four, *Olé*. Five, an ovation from the crowd.

"Now I've got you, now we'll go, come on." Ramón Quintana has not dominated the bull; he has done nothing correctly. A three-year-old bull from the worst ranch in Spain would have killed him on each pass. Fear has kept Ramón's thighs from the lowered horns. Each pass has been accompanied by a violent withdrawal of both legs. However, the movement has been small and quick, and the very existence of a pass, a series of passes, of any nature from a local boy, has drawn an ovation from the crowd. Three easy manoletinas and a series of hesitating derechazos complete the faena. The crowd is delighted. Ramón knows that he has triumphed. The bull is great. He only needed a rest after the banderillas to be great, to catch his wind. Ramón smiles at his father. He loves his father more than ever before in his life and he loves the crowd. The bull charges and tears the boy's pants, exposing his naked buttocks. The crowd laughs. A handkerchief is taped over the bare flesh. The triumph is less. The boy's obvious anger at the indignity amuses the crowd even more. Ramón hates the crowd. He hates his father for having taped the handkerchief on him.

He profiles to kill the bull. The crowd is silent. Ramón goes in. The sword hits bone. Ramón's fear returns. He profiles, goes in again. As the sword sinks deep into the young bull, he raises his head. The boy, who did not cross with the muleta in his left hand to guide the horns away from his body, is hit. He falls, and jumps up. The bull wavers and drops, dying. The crowd applauds. They have seen the boy hit for the second time. He seems all right, though. He is all right. Nothing has happened to him.

The comics have appeared, and a young bull has died in fun. Now Ramón Quintana has killed, and a bull has died in tragedy. It is hard for the children to tell the difference.

Distractedly the crowd applauds. The boy looks for the white handkerchief sign which will give him an ear, the two ears, maybe. The crowd is waiting for the dwarfs to reappear. They do not accord an ear from the yearling bull to the boy who has given almost a half-year's work to entertain them, but their applause is sufficient for the boy to walk and run triumphantly around the ring twice.

Ramón Quintana is all right. He has not triumphed, but he has not had a disaster. The crowd applauded. They liked his performance, and Ramón Quintana is going up. He bows. He walks into the *callejón*. The applause stops, and the dwarfs tumble into the ring dressed as girl acrobats. The crowd has already forgotten Ramón Quintana.

The boy walks around the *callejón* and under the bull ring into the infirmary. He reaches into his trousers. "Please, please," Ramón asks the surgeon, showing him his protruding intestines. "Please."

The *traje de luces* is quickly removed. The boy lies naked on the operating table. The crowd is laughing at the dwarfs.

The doctor examines the boy. The lower abdomen has been pierced to a depth of two inches and torn across for eight inches. A branch of the hypogastric artery has been severed, causing profuse bleeding. The scrotum has been lacerated and the left testicle is bruised. The cord holding the gland has not been damaged, and the gland itself has not burst. The function of the testicle has probably not been impaired. Ramón's father watches in fear as the doctor places clamps on the artery. A sterile towel is laid over his son's exposed bowels. The doctor gives the boy an anesthetic, plasma to alleviate the shock, and an antitoxin to prevent lockjaw.

The manager in the crowd who could have helped Ramón Quintana in his career has left the bull ring and is sitting in a café talking.

"He's not worth anything," a friend says to him.

"I guess not. Too bad. I need a new kid, a good one. I should have kept Cascales, but he looked so bad I let him go. Too bad. Could have made more on him. What I need is one Jiménez, just one."

"We all need Jiménez, my friend, all of us."

Ramón will call on the manager when he gets out of the hospital and will ask to be taken on. The manager will tell him that there are great hopes. He will arrange some fights for Ramón Quintana, if Ramón Quintana will advance a sum to the manager in order to cover certain initial expenses. This sum is only a temporary loan. It will instantly be repaid by the manager as soon as he is able to sign Ramón for a big fight. "In a year, with luck, you can be fighting with Jiménez, Ortega, Romero, anyone you choose," the manager will tell the boy. "On top, in a year. Next year."

Ramón Quintana will work for months. He will give the money he earns to the manager. The manager will steal all his money and, by encouraging the boy with a cheap fight or two a year, the manager will be able to steal from him for a long time.

EIGHT

IT IS A QUARTER to one in the morning. Antonio Romero and his driver Pablo have stopped. The matador has eaten very little on the excuse that the food is bad, and he has delayed their departure by becoming involved in a long conversation with the waiter. Knowing that the matador will not be hungry again until after the bullfight, when his fear is gone, Pablo has urged him to eat. He has tried to ease the growing tension. No reference is made to the fact that the last time Antonio Romero fought in the city toward which they are traveling he was badly wounded. Pablo pays for the dinner and orders himself another coffee.

Manolo Ortega is sleeping. His driver will not disturb him until six o'clock. The Mercedes has traveled 235 miles, less than a third of the trip. Since they reached the high plateau, the Atlantic rain has stopped and the road has become straight. The Mercedes is traveling at an average speed of 65 miles per hour. In order to maintain this average, Manolo Ortega's driver reaches speeds between 90 and 100 miles per hour whenever possible. The roads are empty.

In ten minutes, the show that Francisco Jiménez and Carlos Huerta are attending will be finished. Their picadors have watched the girls and have decided where to go later tonight. They are married men, and they have not been home in two weeks.

Near the theater in the cathedral, Emilio Posada is exhausted and incoherent. He has been before the Virgin for an hour and a half. During the last forty-five minutes he has not risen from his knees. Eight candles have burned out. A blind woman is praying a few feet away from the matador. She is praying not for her lost sight but for the child she is carrying.

Emilio Posada has made his promises. He is empty of words. He remains kneeling as the woman crosses herself and rises to her feet. The empty sound of her cane on the stone floor does not reach the matador. His eyes are closed, his mouth partly opened. He is crying, sixteen and a half hours before he must enter the arena.

It is 1:15.

In the north, Julio Cascales and his cuadrilla leave the city in a single large Packard. The crowd coming from the bull ring delays the matador.

In the infirmary Ramón Quintana is under an anesthetic. For the next two hours the doctor will operate. Peritonitis, resulting from a perforated intestine, could prove fatal.

At 1:45 it is certain that Ramón Quintana will live. His blood pressure has improved and the abdominal wound has presented no difficulties. At 2:30 the abdomen is closed, and the doctor turns to the second injury. He removes the devitalized skin.

Ramón's younger brother is at home. Hidden in a box under his bed are the horns he brought home last night.

Antonio Romero, Manolo Ortega and their cuadrillas are driving south tonight. The cars are crossing the ancient kingdom of Castille. The night is clear. There are no clouds to divide the high plateau from the stars. The night is quiet, and the earth is cold.

The toreros are asleep in their cars, the farmers in their homes. In a few hours the sun will rise and the men from the villages will tend their crops on the scorched land. The sun will burn, the sun will wither the crops. The men will be hungry during the winter. They will sow seeds next spring, and no rain will fall and the sun will burn.

At 3:30 Ramón Quintana is transported in an ambulance from the infirmary at the bull ring to a hospital. The pain will not start until Ramón awakes in the morning when the sun rises and the farmers return to their fields.

Antonio Romero's Chrysler is crossing the Adaja

river. Underneath the bridge, a herd of goats is asleep in the dry river bed. Pablo turns right. The walls of Avila rise directly above the car, black, outlined against the white moon. The car travels along the towered walls that encircle the city.

In the year 1622 a woman from Avila was raised to sainthood. To celebrate this holy event 230 bulls were killed in the plazas of Spain.

Trucks carrying bulls are traveling tonight from the ranches to the cities. Expensive cars are traveling, cars bought by the death of other bulls. At present, the trucks, the bulls, the cars, the men are all in motion. Their routes join, separate, cross and split again. The mountains and the rivers divide. There is no apparent order to the motion, no harmony now between the men and the bulls. In the dark, the men are unable to transform their fear, their cowardice into the honor and courage they will summon this afternoon in the arena. This afternoon the crowd will come to see Antonio Romero, Francisco Jiménez, Manolo Ortega and the Conde de la Corte bulls.

Francisco Jiménez, sitting in a café, thinks of the bulls and is afraid. There is fear in the dreams of Manolo Ortega. There is fear in the eyes of Antonio Romero as he awakes to smoke a cigarette. Pablo is not tired. He has driven almost half the distance that separates the matador from the next bullfight. Pablo knows the road ahead; he has driven it before. Antonio Romero has traveled the same road toward the same city. He has killed there, and he has had luck. He has left in triumph and in dishonor. He has killed, and he has been wounded, and he has left the city in pain.

Pablo is taking the car through the Gredos mountains. The road is dangerous. The matador has stubbed out his cigarette and is waiting for sleep again. Ahead lies the straight road across New Castille, through the huge olive groves and burnt wheat fields. In the valleys below, the villages are quiet. The car turns tightly around the curves. The matador cannot sleep. He looks at his watch. Four o'clock. Another six or seven hours, and I can have a swim and go to bed for a while. The matador reaches for the thermos bottle of hot coffee and closes the window.

He does not think specifically about this afternoon, yet there is a constant fear of death and an awareness of the bulls. Antonio Romero wants to live. He wants to love his young wife again and again and to see his children for a long time. Antonio Romero is afraid.

Pablo drives. A heavy rock falls from the cliff overhead onto the road. Pablo brakes. The matador is thrown to the floor. Pablo looks up and drives on quickly. The matador lies back. An instant of terror reaches into his thoughts. He does not permit the order to focus, the order which could turn the car left toward Madrid, toward his wife. The contract is made. It is no different from countless other contracts he has filled in the past. Tonight, the bullfight will be over, and Pablo will be at the wheel of the Chrysler again.

It was better before Antonio Romero was married, before the children were born. It has always been better in the past. The fact that it is over makes it better. The anxiety is always directed ahead into the afternoons of the next two, three years.

Antonio Romero endures his fear for a reason which has become clear to him three times. Three bulls out of over a thousand, and he has known himself, has learned the distinction between avoiding the horns and accepting them. Three times the bonds have been broken, and the matador has become free to create the faena he knows to be the ideal.

The first time Antonio Romero fought as well as any man ever has, he tried for a month to do it again. During that month he was wounded slightly twice and he received countless indignities from the bulls and the crowd—and he was worse than he had ever been before. And then the ideal occurred a second time. Two years passed during which Antonio Romero rose to be an excellent matador. His performances were consistently good, often great, but the ideal did not return.

Last year, in Valencia, Antonio Romero encountered the ideal for the third time. The obscure desire he had felt since childhood became clear again. The faena his father had spoken of with reverence which seemed inhuman to Antonio was created by the son. He had wondered why the ideal could not be attained every day and had realized that then there would be no limits, no end.

[TEXT CONTINUES ON PAGE 61.]

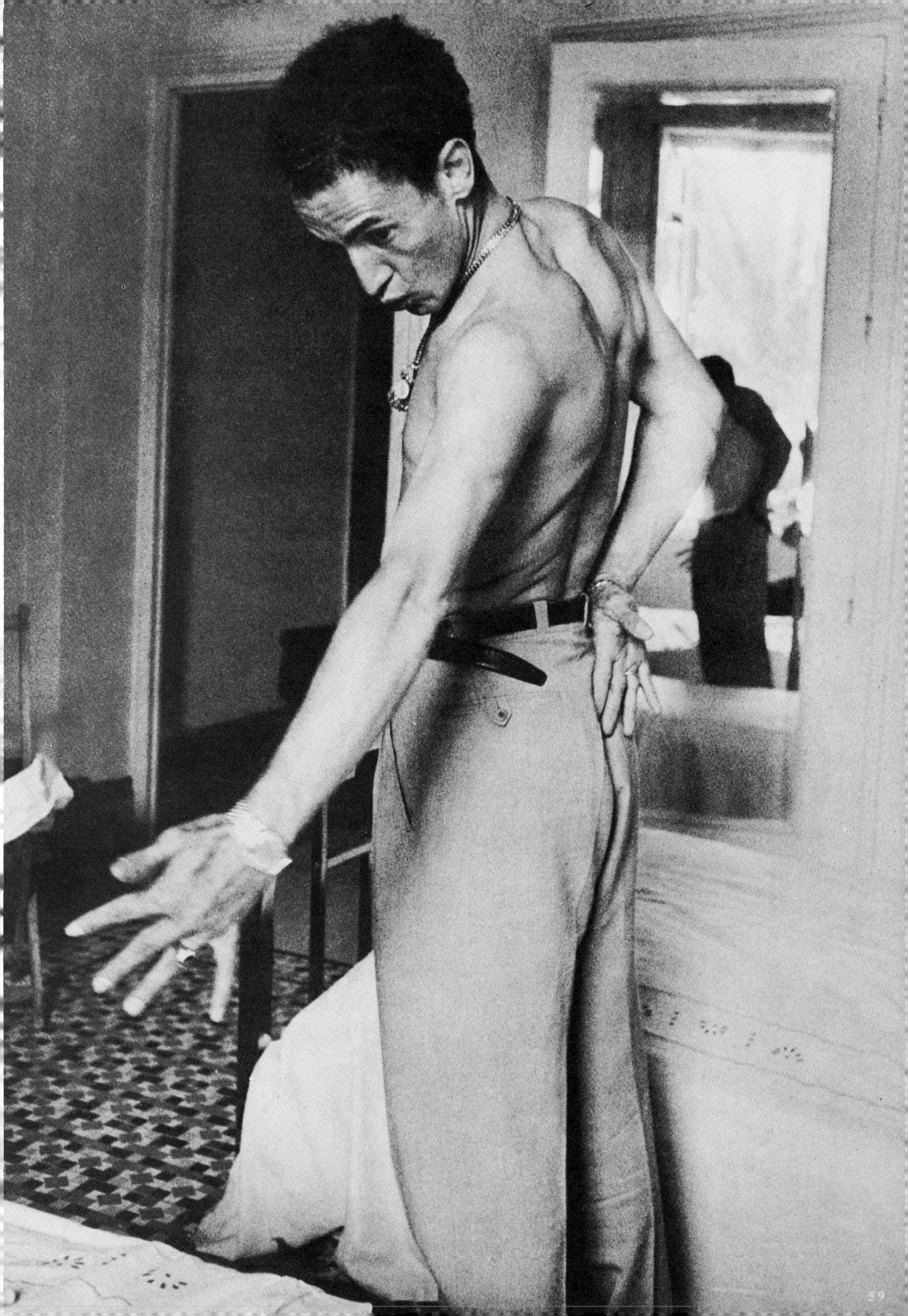

His recollection of the ideal dispels the terror. The first gray of dawn can be seen in the east coming from beyond the sea, beyond Valencia.

Francisco Jiménez has gone to bed. He is afraid, and said so to his friends after the show, in the café, when they mentioned that it was late and that this afternoon there would be a bullfight. As he undressed, Jiménez felt the tension which he fears, the tension over which he has no control when it comes. It has been two weeks since he has felt afraid thirteen hours before a fight. Usually it starts later, nearer the end. He is afraid, and the earlier it starts the worse it becomes.

Down the hall from Jiménez' room, Emilio Posada is in bed. The thought of running away has brought some comfort and he is almost asleep. The night is hot and the matador lies in a messy bed. He kicked the top sheet to the floor. The idea of running away has been replaced by the greatest triumph in the history of the bullfight. Hysterical visions of success replace the thoughts of fear and jail. Endless repetitive shapes of panic cancel the dreams of success, and Emilio Posada turns, rolls over, lies back on his bed, smokes, drinks water and tries to push aside the panic. He throws off the twisted pajamas. Unintelligible forms crowd behind his closed eyes, from which he attempts to free himself, and he puts on the light next to his bed. The forms remain. The matador puts on the light by the door and the ceiling light. He stares at the naked bulbs, and still the forms are in motion behind his vision. His legs contract sharply and he hugs his knees to his chest. Emilio Posada rests his forehead on his knees, and in this position he cries a little.

Across the hall Carlos Huerta returns from the bathroom, removes his silk robe, looks at his watch and goes back to sleep.

NINE

At five o'clock in the morning Manolo Ortega is awake and hungry. He eats a sandwich and watches the dawn. The world seems empty and clean. He can see a hundred miles when he looks out across the brown-and-gray plains. Manolo feels good. This afternoon I'll be the best, the boy says to himself, confident that he controls the power to be good, the power not to be afraid of the horns.

For a month, Manolo Ortega has been the best. For the past week he has felt that no bull could kill him. He is not afraid of the wounds. He knows the doctors are ready. They have been in the past, and they will be. A wound means pain, but the pain goes. A bull cannot kill you when you know you can't die yet. Romero, Jiménez, even his brother Juan, can be killed by the horns, but not Manolo Ortega, not so long as he feels that it can't happen. It makes it easy when you know you are going to live for a long time. It gives you an advantage over the other matadors, over the crowd, even over the bulls, because they must die. When you step in front of the bull and know that in ten minutes he'll be dead and you'll be alive and in a good hotel, it makes life easier.

"*Vámonos*, let's go, let's go, come on, push her along. I'm hungry," Manolo shouts, slapping the seat with the toy riding crop. He opens the window and sticks his head out. The cool morning air rips into his hair, his eyes, his nose. The boy shouts into the wind, whipping the car along. "That's it, faster, wheeee! Faster, faster!"

The speedometer marks 108 miles an hour.

The driver is glad to see the matador free from fear. The quiet, sullen weeks will arrive too soon, when no one will be able to do anything right, when no one will please the head of the cuadrilla who has become afraid. The matador's joy in living excites the driver, convinces him that he too shares the charm, the luck, which protect Manolo Ortega. The speedometer reaches 112 miles. "Wheeee! That's it, let's take off and fly! Come on—come on!" The fierce wind forces the boy to close his eyes, but he remains with his head out of the window, urging the early morning world awake to see the new day.

With a snap, Emilio Posada straightens out his curled body. He lies motionless, and opens his eyes slowly. A ray of sunlight streaks across the room. Posada angrily pulls the heavy curtains closed.

Emilio Posada, matador de toros, feels sick this morning. Naked, he stumbles into the bathroom, drinks four glasses of cold water and sits on the edge of the tub. He is cold, and his body is covered with sweat. Viciously he grabs at the shower curtain and rips it to the floor. He sits on the hard edge of the tub and puts his head on his knees.

Manolo Ortega pulls his head in.

"If there were any bulls this morning, you'd eat them alive, matador," the driver says, smiling.

"I'll eat them this afternoon. I'll cut their ears and their tails too, and I'll kill 'em like this." Manolo jabs toward the windshield with the toy crop and climbs into the front seat. "It's a good car, isn't it, my car." He pats the leather upholstered seats and looks into the glove compartment for some candy. He finds, instead, a pile of old comic books, and the matador settles down comfortably in his $16,000 car to read, as the sun rises over Spain.

"Quack, quack—" Manolo imitates Donald Duck —"Quack." He becomes absorbed in a story which he has read before. Twenty minutes pass. The Mercedes covers twenty-nine miles and slows down in front of a café in a small town. "Come on, matador, let's eat," the driver says. Manolo dumps the comic books on the floor, picks up the riding crop and jumps out, leaving the door open. The driver walks around and closes it.

The matador shies a stone at a pig down the

street and sits at a table in the sun. While he bangs on the metal table with his hands and shouts for the owner, his driver goes inside and asks if they can be served a meal. He mentions the boy's name. Manolo's banging is punctuated with imitations of Donald Duck. The return of the pig to the street inspires the matador to attempt an entire series of barnyard noises. When the café owner comes outside to take his order, Manolo answers him by making sounds suggesting what he wants to eat. His imagination fails and he ends up by saying, "Tomato, onions and olives." The proprietor also notes, "Steak, two eggs, mixed salad."

"For two," the driver adds.

"Give me a sweater, will you?" Manolo asks.

A group of children watches the driver open the trunk of the Mercedes and unpack the matador's suitcase. A thick brown cashmere sweater keeps Manolo's shoulders from the chill air. The children's clothing is ragged and dirty and their bare feet are encrusted with the dust of the street. Their eyes are fixed on the white bread and honey which have been brought to the table. The pig ambles down toward the café, rooting in the gutter with his snout. The children watch Manolo Ortega dip the bread into the bowl of honey. They can see the honey dripping onto the table, onto the ground. The children move closer. The pig snorts around the corner of the building. Suddenly he trots over to the table and rams his mouth into the honey and dust beneath. The owner comes out with a pitcher of hot coffee. Manolo kicks the pig. The owner yells at the children. *"Fuera, fuera!* Get out of here, go on, get out!" he shouts at the children. They and the pig run away together. The owner apologizes to the matador. "If you are bothered again," he urges, "you can sit inside."

"We are all right here," Manolo answers quietly. "We are all right."

When they finish, Manolo says to his driver, "Give me some money and pick me up along the street. I'm going to stretch my legs."

The café owner is disappointed that the matador has wandered off. He had hoped for an autographed picture. The driver pays for the meal, fills the car with gas. He finds Manolo pitching pebbles into a fountain at the other end of town. The children are picking the pebbles up and handing them to the matador. Manolo waves goodbye, and quacks like a duck. The children laugh and run after the Mercedes. Manolo takes a nap. He is full.

When he and his brother, Juan Ortega, were young, they lived in a village where there was no café to serve those who could afford to eat. They had no place to beg.

The *mayoral* of the Plaza de Toros in the south gets out of bed. He buttons his pajamas and walks directly into the corrals. The doorway that separates his bedroom from the six Conde de la Corte bulls is protected on the outside by a thick concrete wall. The *mayoral* is fat, and he has to pull in his stomach in order to squeeze between the protective wall and his house.

The bulls are resting.

The *mayoral* moves along the edge of the corral wall toward the water tap to fill the empty drinking trough. The bulls are alert to the man's motion. Two of the bulls stand. The *mayoral* instinctively judges the distance between himself and the four protected exits from the corral. He moves with decision.

Since the *mayoral* was born on a ranch sixty years ago, he has always lived with bulls. As a boy he helped to brand the calves. As a young man he was determined to be a matador, and succeeded in becoming a second-rate banderillero. Once he worked for a season as a picador but gave it up after being helplessly pinned under the horse as the bull gored. Over his mantelpiece, beneath an image of the Virgin, is a photograph. It shows the *mayoral* pulling a bull's tail, trying to distract the beast from the matador who is struggling on the ground under the horns.

The bulls watch the man limp back across the corral from one safe concrete slab to the next. The limp was given by a bull who caught the *mayoral* behind the right knee the day he decided to be a great banderillero. An inept surgeon turned the wound into a permanent disability. The *mayoral* took a job with a horse contractor and settled in the city. He repaired the giant mattresses which prevent the horns from reaching the horses.

Because of his knowledge of the bulls, the impresarios of the Plaza gave the *mayoral* his present job. In the past, the *mayoral's* wife feared the bulls. She hated them when they wounded her husband, when they wounded her only son, who wants to become a great matador. "The bulls give, and they take away," the *mayoral* repeats to his wife, pointing to the house in which they live.

Before edging into the house, the *mayoral* looks back at the Conde de la Corte bulls. All six are black. Each has a brown area on his back. Their shoulders are heavy, well muscled, their hind quarters are lean. The horns are set wide apart and are uniform in length. Their eyes are clear, their movements acute and decisive. They are five years old. It is a well-matched corrida. The ranch owner has bred the animals scrupulously.

His personal *mayoral* is asleep on a pile of straw in the corridor beside the corral. He will remain with the bulls until they are dead. He will prevent the managers and the impresario from maiming the bulls before the bullfight. The Conde de la Corte bulls will enter the ring this afternoon in their natural state. Their owner permits no shameful disrespect to his bulls. His honor cannot be bought to the advantage of the matadors and their managers.

73, 138, 96, 23, 42, 11: the numbers are branded on the bulls. The *mayoral* calculates this afternoon's corrida. He estimates the number of pics each bull will take; he considers the methods of defense and attack that each will use. The bulls are excellent, and they will prove exacting. If the men cannot overcome their fear they will fail. If the men are ignorant they will fail. The crowd will witness the trial.

A year has passed since the last feria. At noon a cannon will summon the feria. Already posters, pamphlets, and loudspeakers have announced the coming events. A sense of unity will be given by the feria, and in a common search for release the routine will be broken. Invention will replace reality, and for six days an attempt to become free of anxiety and pain will be made. For every dream and fancy there will be an image.

Puppet shows, band concerts, bicycle races, boxing bouts, wrestling matches, swimming contests will succeed one another throughout the days and nights.

In the morning, papier-mâché giants, graciously offered by the municipality, will parade through the streets, and the stature of man will be increased. Ghouls and fiends will follow, to be ridiculed by the adults and beaten by the children. Along the route taken by the images of horror, the hunchbacked, the crippled and the maimed will watch. The idiots will be confused and the blind will listen.

Religious processions will permit the expiation of sins committed during the past year. Men will spend hours on their knees traversing the city, while others carry the image of the Holy Virgin. Their knees will be cushioned to relieve the pain.

On the edge of the city an enormous amusement park has been built. Infinite combinations of sound and movement have been devised in order to amuse and frighten. Horror chambers and roller coasters will permit the crowds to shriek in terror. For a week the terror can be bought for the price of a ride and the shrieks can be in fun. Dishes and glassware can be destroyed or won in a lottery depending upon the choice of amusement.

In the evening, comic operettas and circus clowns will appear in opposition to the tragedy enacted during the late afternoon in the arena.

At night, the constriction of the flamenco will be heard through the laughter of the crowd leaving the amusement park.

In the early hours of the morning, an extravagant display of fireworks will climax the city's daily recreation. Visions of color will burst against the stars. Outrageous detonations will reverberate throughout the city.

TEN

It is 8:30, and the sun is up. In a few hours the heat will begin.

Francisco Jiménez' cuadrilla has left the eastern city in which they fought yesterday. By 10:30 the men will have reached the city to the south toward which Antonio Romero and Manolo Ortega have been traveling all night. Francisco Jiménez is still asleep in his room. In the lobby of the hotel, a group of men from the local Francisco Jiménez Club are waiting for the matador.

On the road, Manolo Ortega has awakened from his nap. The Mercedes has stopped at the entrance to the main square of a small village. Across the road, men are constructing a heavy wooden gate. The matador leans out and shouts. The gate is swung open and the Mercedes goes through the village square which is being transformed into a bull ring for this afternoon's fight.

Today the patron saint of the village will be honored by the death of three small bulls purchased cheaply by the village. The balconies and windows facing the square are decorated with flags and flowers to celebrate the annual event. The City Hall is on the square. At present the bulls are in a stable under the mayor's office. A wooden corridor leads from the stable into the improvised bull ring. The lamppost in the center of the ring will provide safety for the awkward toreros.

The Mercedes passes through the gate at the other end of the square. During the performance this afternoon, all traffic on the main road will stop while a bull is alive in the ring. After each death, the gates will be opened so that the cars can drive through. The gates will be closed again until the next death twenty minutes later.

When he was a child, Manolo Ortega helped to construct the arena in his village. Later he appeared in the ring and in neighboring towns. He began his career this way and was paid nothing. This afternoon he will earn $3,600. In the village where Manolo Ortega was born there are other boys who hope to become matadors. The companions who fought with Manolo Ortega when he was younger have not yet left their village. Manolo Ortega owns an eight-room apartment in the residential district of Madrid, near the French Embassy.

Pablo is driving past the bull ring in a city where Antonio Romero will appear next week. The matador ignores the city at present, as during the night he ignored the bull ring in cities where he has already appeared in recent weeks.

In the country Pablo points out a valley to the matador. It is filled with wheat, and on the gentle slopes there are vast olive orchards. Antonio Romero has been searching for a property to buy when he retires. He wants to invest the money he has earned from the bulls in land and crops. When the two men discuss the future, Pablo's knowledge of the land gives Antonio Romero a feeling of security.

The country is changing. The valleys have become chasms and the slopes have turned to cliffs. They have reached the southern edge of the massive Spanish plateau. Pablo stops to check a tire.

The landscape is barren. Immense mountains of stone can be seen across the empty land. No villages have appeared during the past hour. The world has become an expanse without end. There is no water to soften the broken earth. The air is dry and there are no clouds in the sky. Antonio Romero steps out of the car and walks along the road. In a few hours he will be surrounded by the city and the crowds.

Across the Sahara and over the Atlas Mountains the heat is moving toward Spain. The dead bushes along the road are covered with a layer of white dust. Jagged rocks lie isolated in the blinding light of the sun. Antonio Romero stops. To become part of the world on this road a man must remain motionless and want to die. An imperative desire to move overcomes him. Pablo brings the car up. Antonio Romero sits in the front seat and watches the speedometer.

Francisco Jiménez awakens at ten o'clock, calls down to the concierge and orders his car. His driver comes up and packs while the matador takes a shower. The fear he felt last night after the show has not left him.

At the same time in a hotel room in the next city Francisco Jiménez' sword handler is unpacking. He arrived five minutes ago with the cuadrilla. The sword handler carefully lays out the *traje de luces* for this afternoon, puts fresh linen in the bureau and prepares the matador's altar on a table across from the bed.

Francisco Jiménez orders a large *café au lait* in the lobby and nods in silence at the group of men who surround him. The matador's gestures are quick and his eyes close involuntarily in answer to the eager aficionados. The matador stands and says goodbye politely. His voice is quiet.

The Cadillac sedan is at the door of the hotel. Francisco Jiménez sits next to his driver and whispers to himself, "I am afraid." This morning, the recognition of fear relieves the tension. On the days Francisco Jiménez appears, the tickets go up in price, and because he is the most highly paid the matador feels an obligation to be the most popular. From Jiménez the public demands a performance which will excite their appetite for the spectacular. The violence of the public is in direct relation to their desire, and on the days when Francisco Jiménez does not satisfy he must accept their abuse.

At 10:45 Antonio Romero arrives at the hotel in the south. He has traveled 761 miles since last night at 8:30. The cuadrilla is still on the road.

The hotel lobby, built in a twentieth-century version of Moorish architecture, is filling with aficionados, managers, photographers, critics, sword handlers, ranch owners and impresarios. Sitting on a couch, two matadors are discussing the wounds they have received during the season. They will appear tomorrow with Juan Ortega in the second bullfight of the feria.

At the front desk, two clerks are busy refusing space while trying to register guests with reservations. The concierge and his assistant are trying to satisfy the late demand for tickets to the bullfight. The hotel doorman is helping to park the cars which have brought their owners to the feria. At the airport a plane has landed from Madrid. Passengers who have come for the bullfights are being loaded into the airport bus.

On the way to his room Antonio Romero passes Francisco Jiménez' sword handler in the hall. Pablo brings the suitcases upstairs and the matador puts on his bathing suit and a bathrobe. He goes down to the hotel gardens for a swim. Juan Ortega is showing off his diving skill to a good-looking girl. Antonio Romero nods to Juan Ortega and follows him off the diving board. After the trip the cool water feels good, and Antonio Romero floats for a few minutes before diving again.

Juan Ortega invites the girl for a drink. At the bar beside the pool, two aficionados are reading a bullfight magazine. The matador borrows it and shows the girl a full-page picture of himself on the horns of a bull. He points to a long scar on his left thigh. The girl turns her head away. Juan Ortega laughs at her and orders the drinks. His sword handler finds the matador and informs him that he has been invited to meet the mayor of the city at an official ceremony this evening. Juan Ortega is glad the girl has heard, and he tells her of the house he is building near Madrid and of his swimming pool which will be larger than the one that belongs to the hotel.

The girl turns to speak to a friend standing at the bar on her right. Juan Ortega motions to the bartender to watch, and then leans over to peer intently between the girl's large breasts. He laughs aloud, and as the girl turns back the matador sips his drink.

Manolo Ortega is driving down the main avenue of the city. He has taken the wheel of the Mercedes for the last hour of the trip. In the center of the street a trolley car has stopped to pick up passengers. Manolo weaves through the traffic, driving with his right hand, his left hand hanging out the window. The trolley starts. The matador brings the Mercedes alongside the trolley, reaches out and pinches a woman standing on the steps of the overloaded trolley. Manolo Ortega accelerates instantly. Angrily the woman looks around in surprise. There is no one in sight. The matador howls with laughter. His driver, too, laughs at the total disbelief written on the woman's face as she looks up and down the avenue.

Manolo Ortega drives quickly and makes the tires screech as he turns the sharp corner that leads into the hotel driveway. He stops, jumps out and goes inside.

In another part of the city, Antonio Romero's cuadrilla arrive at their hotel at 11:25 and the men go to their rooms. José Vito immediately returns to the car and leaves for the bull ring, which he reaches at twenty minutes to twelve.

ELEVEN

A LARGE GROUP OF MEN has already gathered for the *apartado*. Most have come directly from the hotel lobby to the bull ring, others are arriving from offices and cafés scattered throughout the city. The ritual of the *apartado* has begun.

The entrance to the patio where the men are meeting is surrounded by a gang of boys. In an open archway the impresario is speaking with the Conde de la Corte. Across the patio, through the arch, the empty arena can be seen. From the authorities the impresario had requested permission for the bullfight to take place. The permission was granted and it has become a command; now the matadors are obliged to appear.

The chief of police is standing in the patio. His captains are near. Four guards are standing on the edge of the crowd holding rifles.

José Vito, *banderillero de confianza* to Antonio Romero, walks directly through the crowded patio to a heavy wooden door in a whitewashed wall. Vito bangs on the door. It is opened briefly, and he is recognized. A metal bolt is shoved aside and the banderillero enters the narrow white corridor which surrounds the corrals. The door is closed. Instantly the activity in the patio is shut out. It is quiet. Voices are lowered and gestures become calculated. The freedom which is apparent outside does not penetrate.

Vito joins Francisco Jiménez' *banderillero de confianza*, who is already in the corridor. The two men watch the bulls through an opening. The six bulls, standing together, sense movement and are alert.

It is ten minutes to twelve. Manolo Ortega's cuadrilla stops at the bull ring on the way to their hotel. It is seventeen hours since they left the bull ring in the north. The matador's *banderillero de confianza* gets out. He is stiff and for a moment feels dizzy as he stands on the sidewalk. He joins the banderilleros in the corrals. The men greet each other in silence. Even Vito's usual exuberance is disciplined.

At a distance above the corrals, above the patio, a crowd is looking down from the Plaza de Toros itself into the corrals at the bulls. From a window in the Plaza, above the infirmary, a four-year-old boy is watching. His mother is inside cooking lunch. His father, who is concierge of the Plaza, is standing with the *mayoral* and the banderilleros in the corridor that surrounds the bulls.

Vito steps through a narrow opening into the corral. He is followed by the other banderilleros. The bulls are nervous. One of the bulls hooks into the direction of the men. The men stand still. Vito pulls a small, worn notebook from his pocket and flips it to a page at the end. Each page has been divided into separate sections by the banderillero. In each section there is a list of six numbers. From corner to corner a large "X" has been drawn across each list. This is a record of the *apartados* which have taken place in the past; this is a record of the bulls killed by Antonio Romero and the matadors who have appeared with him. Vito fills in the next empty space: 138, 73, 11, 42, 23, 96.

Number 73 runs toward the far corner of the corral away from the men, turns, faces them. Number 11 leaves the group of five bulls. He advances slowly toward the men, stops, advances again, stops. The men continue to stand quietly. Vito whispers to Manolo Ortega's banderillero. He makes a note. The *mayoral* appears from another doorway in the corral. The attention of the bulls is divided. The *mayoral* is joined by Juan Ortega. Through thin slits in the walls of the corral, other men are watching the bulls. The police commissioner comes in for a moment, glances at the bulls, returns to the patio. Jiménez' banderillero speaks to Vito. Vito raises his arm suddenly and shouts.

Two of the bulls begin to fight. Number 11 runs

toward Vito. The men slip behind the wall. At the other end of the corral the *mayoral* raises his arms, shouts. Number 11 is now motionless as he watches Vito through the opening in the wall. The bull lowers his head, hooks suddenly at the wall, throwing the hard plaster into the air. He backs away a short distance, charges, backs away and charges again. The *mayoral* throws a stone in the direction of the bull to incite him to charge. The bull runs toward the *mayoral,* who slips to safety, and Vito re-enters the corral with the other banderilleros.

A cannon report can be heard in the distance announcing the feria. It is noon. In the cafés, drinks are ordered, and the crowds move more quickly for a moment.

Manolo Ortega's banderillero walks down the corridor. He joins Juan Ortega. The matador gestures toward Number 11 and Number 138.

Two aficionados, friends of Francisco Jiménez, leave the corridor and return to the patio. They have seen the bulls. Every time the door is opened men try to enter the door to the corrals. They try to impress their own importance, or their intimacy with someone of importance, upon the *mayoral's* assistant who guards the door to the corrals. Whoever exits from the door is immediately questioned concerning the bulls. The men who have been near the bulls are followed through the crowd. The talk in the patio is solely about the bulls.

For twenty minutes the banderilleros study the Conde de la Corte bulls, and then they pair them: 23—96, 73—42, 138—11. The decision is difficult, as the corrida is unusually well matched. The banderilleros note which bulls have horns that curve in, and attempt to determine which will be the least dangerous bulls, which bulls are not cowardly; they note which bulls are the smallest, which in the best physical condition. Opposite these, they place the bulls with the longest, widest horns, the bulls who do not charge honestly, the bulls who seem to present particular difficulties. Their judgment is usually correct.

The *mayoral* remains in the corridor and the banderilleros leave. They walk directly through the crowded patio into a small room. The one window is closed, and the thick metal blinds are shut. The police commissioner is sitting at a plain wooden table. The impresario of the Plaza is seated next to him. Overhead a single light bulb is burning. The small room fills with the three banderilleros, Jiménez' manager, Manolo Ortega's manager, Juan Ortega, two police captains, the *mayoral's* assistant, a representative from the Conde de la Corte's ranch, an old matador from the city who retired thirty years ago, two delegates from the Provincial Governor's office, a single critic, and two aficionados who belong to the nobility.

A packet of cigarette paper is drawn from someone's pocket and three transparent slips are removed. On each, a pair of numbers is written:

23—96
73—42
138—11

Each slip of paper is crushed into a minute ball. No one speaks. In the room, someone takes off his hat. The three bits of paper are placed inside. Another hat is placed over it. For an instant the hats are gently shaken together. Vito puts his right hand between the two hats. His finger tips feel for the paper.

The patio is filled with men talking and arguing.

On the steps leading from the sidewalk down to the patio, a blind man is being led by a boy. The boy is jostled by the crowd and he loses his grip on the man's hand. The boy is pushed aside and the blind man stumbles down the stairs into a group of aficionados.

Vito pulls his hand out. Delicately his fingers unfold the paper. The men who cannot see the paper watch his face. The paper is opened. 23–96: Antonio Romero, matador de toros, will kill these bulls this afternoon.

Manolo Ortega's banderillero reaches into the hat. The second paper is opened: 11–138. Juan Ortega smiles. Although he does not like Number 11, he believes Number 138 will permit his brother to create an excellent faena. The *sorteo* is finished. The third paper is thrown to the floor unopened. Francisco Jiménez will fight numbers 73 and 42.

The names of the men and the numbers of the bulls they will fight are registered opposite one another on a printed form. The room empties and the light is turned off.

The boy has found the blind man and led him to his destination.

A sudden movement animates the crowd of men in the patio. The armed police station themselves at the foot of the stairs which lead to the narrow walks above the corrals. Orders are given. Men are stationed inside the Plaza de Toros above the *chiqueros*. The *mayoral* instructs his assistants. The officials of government and police climb the stairs. The banderilleros and managers follow. They are joined by the men whose function or position permitted them to enter the corrals before the *sorteo*. Within a few minutes, the narrow walks above the corrals are filled. At the foot of the stairs a crowd is trying to push its way up. The police attempt to end arguments by closing the metal grille at the top.

From above, thirty bulls can be seen in separate corrals. Each corrida is enclosed by white walls. The corrals are connected by massive wooden gates. A system of ropes permits the gates to be opened from the safety of the walks.

Immediately on the left, the Carlos Nuñez bulls for tomorrow's corrida are alert. Farther away, the bulls from the ranches of Don Juan Cobaleda and Don Alipio Pérez are resting in the sun. To the right six Miura bulls are moving nervously. Other corrals enclose oxen with tremendous horns or small yearling bulls for the nocturnal fights.

The Conde de la Corte bulls are directly below on the left. A gate swings open and four oxen join the Conde de la Corte corrida. Another gate is opened leading to a small, empty corral at the foot of the Plaza. The oxen start through the second open gate. The bulls are excited by the shouts of the *mayoral,* who is standing in a corner of their corral. The bulls run and hook at each other and at the oxen. Number 138 approaches the open gate through which the oxen are moving. The bull goes halfway through the gate. The rope is held ready. The bull backs away furiously and joins Number 11, who is in the center of the corral.

The operation is repeated. The second time, Number 73 follows the oxen into the empty corral. The gate slams behind the bull, and he is cut off from the corrida. A gate is opened into another corral and the oxen begin to leave. As the oxen move, Number 73 attempts to follow. The gate is slammed and Number 73 is isolated. The bull swings his body into the confining corners of the small corral and braces himself on his hind legs, ready to charge. He is alone, and he becomes infuriated. A gate is opened. The dark corridor which leads into the Plaza de Toros is exposed. Number 73 charges into the opening and the gate crashes closed.

Underneath the Plaza, the bull charges down a wide corridor. Eight thick metal doors face the corridor. At the other end, straight ahead, is the gate which leads into the arena. Number 73 finds one of the eight doors open. He continues his charge through the open metal door. The door clangs shut. The bull whirls around. It is quiet, and the light is dim. The walls of the *chiquero* are whitewashed. They are pitted at the level of the bull's horns. The Plaza de Toros is seventy-eight years old.

The blinding noonday sunlight is evenly spread over the open arena. As the shadows begin to lengthen during the hot afternoon, the bull's rage will spend itself in isolation and darkness.

Outside in the corrals the oxen have betrayed another bull—Number 11. The bull has entered the small corral, but in the split instant in which the man pulls the rope to crash the gate closed, the bull has twisted about and struck the gate with one of his horns. The massive gate is viciously flung open. The bull pursues his object and crashes the gate against the wall. Repeated blows shred the heavy planks. The gate is motionless. The bull withdraws. In a fury, he renews his attack. The horns cut into the wall, and a spray of whitewashed stone and plaster is flung into the air. The men on the walk are conscious of the power beneath them.

The oxen rejoin the remaining four Conde de la Corte bulls. Number 96, Antonio Romero's bull, is betrayed. He charges into the small corral and underneath the Plaza into a *chiquero*. He is followed by Number 23, Romero's second bull.

Number 138 is standing quietly. A fifteen-foot pole is used to jab his flanks and incite him to charge into the darkness. Number 138 raises his head. He ignores the pole and the oxen. Alone and with dignity the bull enters the empty corral and walks slowly under the Plaza into the open *chiquero*.

There is no display of power or courage. Juan Ortega has observed carefully. This is Manolo Ortega's bull.

Number 42 is alone with Number 11. The two bulls lock horns. Their rage is being spent on each other. The *mayoral* becomes concerned; the bulls are his responsibility. He goes into the corral and throws a stone at the bulls. They are distracted by his movements. Ropes are pulled. The oxen re-enter. Number 42 is deceived. His shoulder is jabbed and he, too, charges under the Plaza. A rope is pulled from above, a metal door opens, crashes closed. Number 42 is in the *chiquero.*

All activity is stopped. Number 11 must be given time to rest. The bull may damage his horns on the walls if his rage does not diminish. If a horn is broken, the bull will be rejected. Five minutes pass in silence. A gate is slowly opened. Number 11 watches. Three oxen join the bull. The bull throws one of the oxen to the ground, inflicting a large wound. The ox will be butchered. The oxen walk into the small corral. Number 11 follows. The oxen leave. Number 11 looks up at the motionless circle of men directly above his horns. The gate is opened. A long pole is slowly brought near the bull's flank. He cannot see the pole. He is struck. A powerful charge carries the bull into the open *chiquero.* The last metal gate crashes behind Manolo Ortega's first bull.

The bulls are alone. For five years they have lived together on the range. Tonight their stripped carcasses will hang together next to the corrals in which the Carlos Nuñez bulls will be resting.

It is 12:45.

The *apartado* is finished. The walk, the corrals, the patio are empty. The men disperse into the city.

TWELVE

JOSÉ VITO has left the Plaza de Toros. He moves quickly through the heavy crowds toward the Cathedral. In the streets a religious procession is forming. There are no individuals during the feria; outside the immense cathedral a throng presses toward the miraculous Virgin. Vito buys two candles. They are the same length as the banderillas he will use this afternoon. He holds them above his head, one in each hand, and imitates the act of placing the banderillas, the act which supports his family.

The banderillero moves gracefully as he enters the Cathedral. Under the colossal vaulted dome a dense mass is in adoration. The faithful advance in a long line, intent upon kissing the pedestal that raises the Virgin above their eyes. There is resignation in their movements.

Vito can see the Virgin at a distance. His fingers brush the holy water. He crosses himself, walks the length of the Cathedral and stops before the chapel of San Antonio, the patron saint of his village.

The banderillero holds the candles in his right hand. He strikes the ends of the candles against the wall of the Cathedral to make sure they are even with each other. This afternoon he will hit the banderillas against the barrera in the same manner. Carefully Vito places the two candles before San Antonio, minutely adjusting them so that they are exactly perpendicular to the floor and parallel to each other. When they are perfectly straight, Vito stands back.

He lights the candles and kneels in prayer. He prays for the child his wife bears, the child which she may deliver today. To the father, the candles now represent the straight path through life which the child must follow and the straight back he must have. The father prays to San Antonio that the symbolic value of the candles will become manifest in the infant. The banderillero looks up at the saint, readjusts one of the candles and leaves the Cathedral.

Francisco Jiménez has arrived in the city and has gone for a walk with a friend. On his way back to the hotel he passes a shoe store, sees some moccasins he likes in the window and tries the door of the shop. It is locked. The owner is inside. He opens the door and tells the matador that the store is closed until six o'clock. "Come back this evening; they'll still be here." The door is closed.

Fake flowers, growing in fake earth in fake pots, are for sale, with potato chips, toy mice and paper hats. A legless woman in an ambulatory chair is stationed on the sidewalk selling cigarettes. The matador asks for a pack of Chesterfields. The woman puts a beer bottle down on the floor of her chair and offers the matador another brand. "There are no Chesterfields, señor. These are very good; they are better."

Francisco Jiménez is approached by a leprous seller of lottery tickets. On every corner there are lottery tickets for sale. The matador does not want any. He is trying to make his way through the crowds back to the hotel.

"Tres millones, tres millones, three millions, millions, millions." The tickets are shoved at the matador.

"Peseta, peseta, peseta, peseta, peseta, peseta, para la Virgen." A blind salesman chants his offer of pink or light-blue plastic pins representing the Virgin, which he sells for a penny.

The matador turns to his friend and hurries him. "Come on, come on!"

The Virgin can be bought everywhere; she is offered in sizes from an inch to four feet, in paper, wood, cheap metal, silver-gilt, or solid silver, depending upon the purse or faith of the client. A dozen shoeshine men obstruct the sidewalk in front of every café.

"Come on."

Near the hotel, in front of a men's club, the members are sitting comfortably in wicker armchairs. They are neither drinking nor eating. Every day, for years, they have sat in their particular chairs. The men watch the crowds go by. During the feria every chair is occupied. A few of the men wave to Francisco Jiménez, but the matador does not see them and the men do not rise.

Some boys have started a newspaper fire in the gutter. At the corner, a delivery is being made to a butcher shop. A little girl pulling a toy mouse on a string crosses in front of Francisco Jiménez. A group of students march by, arm in arm, singing. One of them bumps the matador and accidentally steps on the little girl's toy and crushes it. The child holds up the string and cries.

Francisco Jiménez reaches the hotel and goes directly to his room.

It is 1:15 in the afternoon.

In the lobby Juan Ortega is arguing with another matador. He sits with his feet on the coffee table in front of him.

"If you don't put your feet down I'll leave," the other matador says.

"I'll put my feet where I want." And Juan Ortega knocks over a coffee cup with the toe of his shoe. The other matador stands up, and Ortega insults him vilely.

Two friends join Juan Ortega. They sit on either side of him and hold his arms gently. Juan Ortega makes an obscene gesture at the matador who is standing and calls him a pimp. "You're afraid of me," he adds nastily.

"I am a gentleman and we are friends, Juan," the matador says. "You cannot force me to act like a swine just because you have no manners." He turns to leave.

Juan Ortega tries to stand, but his two friends hold him tightly on the couch. An hour ago Juan Ortega learned that the girl he loves has been sent out of the country by her parents. The girl's father is a wealthy ranch owner. There is no possibility that he will permit her to marry Juan Ortega.

Juan Ortega's driver walks through the lobby, and the matador calls him over to find out if the wine has been delivered to his new house outside Madrid.

"*Sí*, matador, it was delivered yesterday, fifty cases."

One of the men on the couch stands and walks away with the driver. "What does he need fifty cases of wine for?" the friend asks. "He never drinks it."

"You think the wine is something? Come out to the house sometime and see the stuff. There's enough Coca-Cola, beer, whiskey, cognac, for all of Spain. Everywhere he goes, I am told, 'Buy, buy, buy.' Yesterday I bought forty-five bath towels and six dozen cups. Last week it was blankets, dishes, and soap, enough soap to wash yourself twenty times a day. Soap is his favorite, in all colors and all sizes. Every bathroom in the house has a cabinet full of soap in it. If I say anything he gets mad. Now he wants to know about the wine again—I told him last night the wine had been delivered."

"He's got the money, let him buy it," the friend says.

"You're right, let him buy it, but it's still crazy to buy all this stuff. It'll take forever to use it up. His girl has gone, you know. He's going to be worse. You saw him just now. Her father won't let him marry her."

The matador has often been invited to the girl's home and he has practiced with the young bulls on her father's ranch. He has lived there as a guest and a friend of her father's and the girl has grown to love him. Juan Ortega is one of the wealthiest young men in Spain, and he will not be allowed to marry the girl he loves.

Manolo Ortega joins his brother on the couch. They read the news of yesterday's bullfights in the papers. They skip over the other matadors: Juan reads his reviews first and then those of Manolo; Manolo reads about himself and then about his brother. The reviews are excellent and the brothers are satisfied.

"How are the bulls?" Manolo asks.

"Big. The second one is good—the first, no. Keep yourself for the second—138—big, strong, horns are good, brave. You can cut the ears on this one."

At 1:30 the lobby is jammed.

In four hours the bullfight will start. Throughout the hotel there is a nervous sense of immediacy which will reach its climax at 5:30. The hotel staff will not attend the bullfight, yet their actions are infected with a strange intensity.

In the lobby, words which are usually without

significance become urgent. Before going to lunch, the critics are given their tickets by the sword handlers and tomorrow's reviews are assured. Among the customers in the café opposite the hotel, gaiety is underlined with apprehension.

Four hours separate the city from the bullfight. In an effort to escape the intense heat, the crowds have left the streets. The amusement park is empty, and throughout the city shops are closed. The papier-mâché giants and fiends are stored away until tomorrow morning's parade. The last customers in the cafés run from the shade of one building to the next on their way home. Windows and blinds are latched against the fierce light. The city has retreated in a desperate attempt to avoid the choking heat. The heat is dry. It draws moisture from the earth and leaves it cracked. The heat is oppressive and men crave sleep, yet it excites and forbids rest.

At three o'clock the city appears completely deserted. No one is in the pool behind the hotel; there is no one in the lobby. The head concierge has gone to bed, and at the telephone swichboard the operator is knitting to keep awake. The assistant clerk at the front desk counts the number of black tiles in the floor design that separate his chair from the hotel manager's office. The doorman is asleep on a stool in a corner of the entrance. Outside in the garden four taxi drivers are stretched on the lawn in the shade of a palm tree. The hot wind has died away.

It is 3:30, two hours before the bullfight.

The wide corridors in the hotel are empty. Antonio Romero is asleep in room 208. On the third floor, Francisco Jiménez is lying on his bed in room 320. Down the hall, Manolo Ortega lies asleep in room 328. The rooms are dark, and the men are naked.

Under the Plaza de Toros the bulls are in their individual *chiqueros.* The light is dim. Number 138 is rubbing his horns against the metal door. The immense shadow which divides the Plaza into sun and shade is moving slowly across the sand.

THIRTEEN

MANOLO ORTEGA, matador de toros, awakens. He stares into the darkness and wipes his eyes. His cheeks are wet. He presses his lips together and straightens his legs. The dream is forgotten but the fear remains. In the dark the boy searches for the overpowering confidence he felt this morning at dawn. Manolo yawns, stretches out on the bed and rubs his hand along his body. He twists his head to loosen the pain he feels in his neck muscles.

From his brother's room next door the boy can hear the voices of men talking. Through a crack in the shutters, a thin streak of sunlight reaches across his naked body and catches the hard gold embroidery on the jacket that rests over the back of a chair. Manolo Ortega stands up. The sun is caught in a cluster of gold medals which he wears on a gold chain around his neck to protect him from the horns. Manolo puts on the small light next to his bed. He picks up the heavy gold watch his brother gave him on the day of his alternativa, looks at it and puts it down. He crosses the room, listens at the door, hesitates and opens it.

His brother is sitting with three friends.

"Qué tal, Manolito?" Juan Ortega asks.

"Bien, bien," Manolo answers, blinking into the bright sunlight. The boy puts on a bathrobe, picks up his riding crop, and joins the men. His sword handler comes in from the hall, gently clapping his hands in a soft flamenco rhythm.

"Ola, Miguel." The boy greets the older man and claps his hands to the rhythm. Miguel begins to sing. Manolo's manager and a friend come in. They sit on the edge of the bed next to Manolo. Through the open door into his room Manolo Ortega can see the images of his faith, the images of the Christ and the Virgin repeated on the altar Miguel has arranged.

It is four o'clock. In an hour, Manolo Ortega will offer his prayers.

Miguel claps his hands louder. Manolo taps his riding crop in time with the rhythm. Miguel starts another song, his voice fills the room. He sings of the little things of love that bring laughter. Juan Ortega stamps his heels and claps his hands loudly. The aficionados and the manager join in an ever-quickening rhythm. Manolo Ortega jumps from the bed and makes a mock pass at an imaginary bull whose horns cannot kill. He maintains the rhythm with his hands. Suddenly he grabs his riding crop and leaps on an armchair. He reaches high toward the ceiling with the toy.

"Look, look, I can touch it!" Manolo yells. He loses his balance and falls on the bed. The men laugh. The room is filled with the sound of song and rhythm and men giving expression to their joy.

It is 4:30 in the afternoon. In one hour the bullfight will start. The shadow cast by the Plaza de Toros has lengthened, and throughout the city there is an awakening.

Manolo Ortega's driver has left the room and has driven to the hotel where the cuadrilla is dressing. The picadors are ready in the lobby. The hotel owner's little girl is sitting on the lap of one of the picadors, kicking with her heels at the metal armor he wears on his right leg to see if it hurts. The picador smiles. He puts the little girl down and stomps awkwardly down the steps with his companions. The picadors sit stiffly in the huge Hispano and are driven to the Plaza de Toros.

Antonio Romero turns off the shower and oils his thick black hair. He combs it carefully. Two friends are talking quietly in the matador's room. One of the men is a department-store owner. Last spring Antonio Romero spent two weeks in his home recuperating from the wound he suffered in this city. The matador comes out of the bathroom and joins his friends. There is no apparent tension, and for a while the three men talk of the land Antonio Romero wants to buy, and of his family.

"I saw your wife yesterday, Antonio, and the children. Carmencita has grown since I saw her in San Sebastián a month ago. She's adorable. I promised to bring her a rabbit when I get back after the feria."

The matador's sword handler lights a candle on the altar. Antonio Romero has disciplined his fear. He acts with the knowledge that he may die within the hour and with the dignity of a man who has learned to accept death. A breeze from the window blows the curtains. Antonio Romero stands to dress for the bullfight. On the altar, the candle is burning. In Madrid, three years ago, during the feria of San Isidro, the last rites were administered to Antonio Romero. On the 7th of July, two months later, he fought in Pamplona.

Francisco Jiménez puts away his electric razor. His sword handler is ready. The matador stands. He is wearing pajama trousers; his thin chest is bare. The sword handler places the heavy black montera on the matador's head, twists a few hairs together at the back, and attaches the coleta. Francisco Jiménez removes his trousers and stands naked. There are already nine men in the matador's room. The Duke of Valdemoro is sitting in the armchair watching. The door into the hallway is open. Men are constantly coming in to see Francisco Jiménez dress for the bullfight. The room is crowded and the matador can barely move about, yet he says nothing. Jiménez' manager pushes into the room and asks the men to leave. They appeal to the matador, hoping he will ask them to stay. Francisco Jiménez raises his eyes, looks at them, and tells his sword handler to make sure the stockings are smooth under his knee. The manager asks a friend to stand at the door and see that no one is allowed to come in.

The Duke of Valdemoro asks the manager for a cigarette, then addresses the matador. "How was the show last night, Francisco?"

"Fine." The matador smiles and turns around. "There was a girl in a red dress who danced." He continues dressing. He closes his eyes tightly and shouts at his sword handler. "That's too tight, idiot!" The outburst is sudden, vicious; then the matador relapses into silence.

"I hear you didn't go to bed till four." There is a tone of reproach in the Duke of Valdemoro's voice.

"I wasn't tired," the matador answers curtly. "I slept late this morning," he adds, smiling.

It is a quarter to five. Manolo Ortega is absorbed in the rhythm of the flamenco. Laughter, voices, song, swell and occupy the room. The room is flooded with sunshine. "It is time, matador," Miguel says.

The song has ended. The room has become empty. Manolo Ortega walks into his own room and says aloud, "I am afraid." He takes a quick shower and at five minutes to five he is ready to dress. "I am afraid."

The matador throws his towel on the floor. "I am afraid," he says. He sits naked on the edge of the bed. Miguel slips a pair of thin cotton trousers over the boy's legs. "I am afraid."

The words expand into the silence and remain. The men in the room are rendered impotent by the words. They cannot help the boy. They have the desire, but they cannot act. Manolo Ortega is isolated within his fear.

Miguel slips a long pair of pink stockings over the matador's legs. He slips a second pair over the first. The cotton trousers are tied below the knee. The matador stands up.

"I am afraid."

Miguel holds the white-and-gold silk trousers open. The matador steps into them. They are tight. The matador struggles to pull them to his waist.

"I am afraid."

There is no answer to the words.

Antonio Romero's banderilleros are getting into the black Hispano. They are being driven to the hotel through the crowded streets. The city is awake.

Antonio Romero is praying. He is dressed in purple and gold. His body is erect; only his head is bowed before the holy images.

Francisco Jiménez is putting on his black slipper-shoes. He stands before the mirror and adjusts the red ribbon tie over his crisp white frilled shirt.

It is 5:08.

The stands in the Plaza de Toros are half filled. In front of the hotel a crowd has gathered.

Manolo Ortega's manager is standing before a small table. There are forty-two holy images before him. Gently he touches the images in an ordered ritual. He prays. The images are touched in a reverse order, and the ritual is ended.

"I am afraid."

Manolo Ortega's cuadrilla has arrived at the hotel. The telephone rings in the matador's room. The sword handler answers. He hangs up immediately. "The car is here."

It is 5:09.

Francisco Jiménez is praying. An aficionado has pushed his way into the room and is talking while the matador prays. The aficionado lights a cigar. The matador bends forward to kiss an image of the Christ. The manager whispers to the aficionado, "Shut up."

It is 5:10.

Manolo Ortega is dressed in white silk. His shoulders are thickly studded with gold. There is gold on his chest and on his back. There is gold along the white silk that covers his thighs.

The manager's wife enters.

"I am afraid." The boy can find no other words. He utters them not as a plea but in recognition of his fear. The manager's wife holds the matador to her breast and embraces him. He kisses her and is unwilling to let her go. The woman leaves, closing the door behind her. Juan Ortega kisses his brother and leaves.

It is 5:11.

Francisco Jiménez is waiting for the elevator.

Antonio Romero is crossing the lobby.

"*Suerte,* matador."

"*Suerte.*"

"*Suerte.*"

"*Suerte,* Antonio, *suerte.*"

"*Suerte.*"

Friends and aficionados are hurrying into their cars, into waiting taxis. A man runs frantically through the lobby and up the stairs to find the tickets he has forgotten.

Antonio Romero, matador de toros, sits in the back seat of the Hispano between two of his banderilleros. Vito and the sword handler are in the front seat beside the driver. The manager, a photographer and a friend occupy the remaining seats. A local assistant sword handler is standing on the running board. The driveway is full. The Hispano moves slowly. It is hot. Friends call in through the open windows.

"*Suerte,* Antonio."

"*Suerte.*"

"*Suerte.*"

Francisco Jiménez is riding down in the elevator. He crosses the lobby quickly, ignoring the men, the hands, the acclaim given him by the crowd.

From the narrow back streets of the city, crowds join the traffic along the main avenues and hurry toward the Plaza. Trains, buses, trolleys, taxis, private cars and pedestrians converge upon the circle formed by the arena in the center of the city.

In the cafés, customers hurriedly pay for their drinks.

On the rooftops of the buildings that adjoin the Plaza de Toros, crowds have gathered to see half or a quarter of the bullfight, depending upon the height of the building. In the streets below a crowd has formed to see the people entering the Plaza. Those who will attend the bullfight are watched by those who will not. The Plaza is filling through a dozen entrances. Each entrance is surrounded by a pack of boys eagerly hoping to get in. To handle the vast crowd, the city police are augmented by the national and provincial police. White uniforms salute green uniforms, green salute khaki, and all colors come to attention and salute the government officials as they arrive in their cars.

In the patio beside the corrals, the picadors are being helped onto their horses. The ears of the horses are stuffed with newspaper; their eyes are covered, their bodies dulled with morphine. The horses stand awkwardly under their huge mattresses. In one of the *chiqueros* a bull hooks at the wall with his right horn and dislodges a stone.

"I am afraid." Manolo Ortega stands before the images and prays.

The doctors inspect the infirmary, check their instruments and walk into the *callejón.*

Manolo Ortega crosses himself.

It is 5:15.

Antonio Romero is silent. From a distance the crowd recognizes the great leather basket that holds the capotes and the muletas on top of the Hispano. In a corner of the rack a water jug is held firmly in place. Six swords rest in a heavy leather sheath which the sword handler holds between his knees.

The men inside the car form a unit separate from the city. They are adorned in pink, in green and silver, in red and purple and gold. In the eyes of the crowd, searching out the brilliance as the car passes, is an expression of envy and adoration. Whenever the car is slowed by the traffic, men run alongside it and shout words of encouragement at the matador, words which are ignored.

Vito passes a cigarette to the matador. The car reaches the gate at the Plaza de Toros. The gate opens. The car is driven inside through the crowd.

It is 5:20.

Manolo Ortega is leaving the hotel.

"*Suerte,* matador."

"*Suerte.*"

"*Suerte.*"

Francisco Jiménez is being driven to the Plaza de Toros. Along the way, the blind stand, shrieking figures that reach into millions. The millions can be won if the right number is selected in the national lottery. The blind do not know the numbers, which are pinned to their lapels and dresses. The maimed offer their atrocity to the charity of the crowd.

Francisco Jiménez arrives at the Plaza de Toros. The Conde de la Corte is helped to his seat at the barrera. Among the crowd in the street, scalpers are hawking their last tickets.

It is 5:25.

On the third floor of a hospital in the north, Ramón Quintana is receiving a visit from his family. His younger brother has spent the afternoon in the sun holding a muleta before an imaginary bull. Ramón Quintana's mother is crying. The doctor examines the wounds made by the yearling bull. He assures the mother that her son will be all right.

The candles Vito offered to San Antonio have burned out.

The lobby of the hotel is empty.

Manolo Ortega arrives at the Plaza de Toros.

"*Suerte,* Manolo."

"*Suerte.*"

It is 5:26.

In the *callejón* the leather baskets have been opened. Spread over the barrera in a neat row, the pink-and-yellow capotes are ready. The names of the men who will use them are stamped in black on the yellow side. In a rack near the *toril* the pics are in order. Their thick, sharp steel points are covered with vaseline. Official stamps are glued near the guard on the long wooden shaft. The steel points glisten in the sun. In a row of garish color, the banderillas are hanging from their barbs on a wire, their tips covered with corks.

The crowd is intent upon the clock above the Plaza de Toros. Protected from the sun, in the dark entrance to the arena, Antonio Romero, Francisco Jiménez and Manolo Ortega are carefully adjusting their *capotes de paseo.* The local press is busy with cameras and pencils. The critics from Madrid are seated in the shade.

It is 5:28.

High above the arena of sand, the President of the bullfight takes his seat. Immediately beside him sits a retired matador who will advise. The bandmaster is standing in front of the band, his baton in his right hand. He is watching the President. The stands are full.

Antonio Romero shuffles his feet in the sand.

Francisco Jiménez blinks his eyes into the sun.

Manolo Ortega wets his lips and stares at the empty arena.

The bandleader raises his baton.

It is 5:30.

The trumpets proclaim the bullfight.

FOURTEEN

THE MATADORS cross themselves as they step forward into the sun. In the ritual there is relief from fear. The crowd applauds. The band is playing a *paso doble.*

Dressed in black, the *alguacil* rides slowly ahead of the men in gold. The circle of sand is split by the shadow of the Plaza into sun and shade. The sun is reflected in the gold, and the men in gold walk with dignity and stature. In grotesque contrast to the elegance of the toreros on foot, the picadors and their mounts move in a ponderous and misshapen manner across the sand.

Antonio Romero, Francisco Jiménez, Manolo Ortega step into the shade together. Purple and gold, yellow and gold, white and gold, they move in unison, followed by their banderilleros in flaming colors. The toreros accept the ovation given them by the crowd.

Gaily decorated with bells and colored tassels, a team of mules crosses the sand, and the procession ends. The mules will drag the dead bulls from the arena.

Below the President's balcony the *alguacil* stops. Sweeping his yellow-plumed hat to one side, he bows and gallops quickly around the arena.

The crowd is seated half in the sun, half in the shade. During the afternoon they will express their fury, their avarice, their monstrous demands and ignorant hopes, their fear and their adoration. In their rage and in their devotion they will be bound together in a mass, or they will split in opposition and turn their violence upon each other.

The matadors bow to the President. In exchange for the ornate *capotes de paseo* they have worn for the procession, they are handed their capes over the barrera by the sword handlers standing in the *callejón.* Antonio Romero swings his cape in the air, his eyes on an imaginary bull. Francisco Jiménez nods to the Duke of Valdemoro. Manolo Ortega walks through the nearest *burladero* and stands next to his brother. He is jostled by a soft-drink vendor, eager to make his sales before the first bull appears.

The *callejón* is full. Managers, doctors, police officials, friends of the impresario, all take their places behind the protective walls. Picadors, banderilleros, ring attendants, butchers are waiting for the moment they will act.

Above the *callejón,* honoring those individuals in the front row to whom they have been given, the *capotes de paseo* are brilliantly displayed. Christ looks up and red roses are surrounded by green leaves and sequins. The Holy Virgin looks down and on her silken cheeks pearls resemble tears.

Men and women in the first rows attempt to reach the matadors with words of friendship and encouragement.

"Suerte, Antonio."

"Qué tal, Francisco?"

"Ola, Manolo, *Ola!"*

Francisco Jiménez speaks to his friends, Manolo Ortega smiles quickly in answer, Antonio Romero raises his hand; yet an infinite distance exists between the *callejón* and the crowd. From behind the safety of steel cables a hand reaches down and claps Antonio Romero on the shoulder.

"Suerte, Antonio."

The matador looks up, smiles and says, *"Gracias."*

The *alguacil* gallops across the arena, receives from the President the order to release the first bull, and gallops to the *toril.* Inside the *burladeros* around the ring Antonio Romero's banderilleros are standing. The *alguacil* hands the symbolic key to the keeper of the *toril* gate. The *alguacil* gallops from the arena. Antonio Romero presses the montera tightly onto his head, bringing it to the level of his eyebrows. The matador holds his cape gathered together. The circle is closed.

The Plaza de Toros is open to the blue sky. The fierce light of the sun burns into the arena and only the empty circle below can be seen from the stands.

In semidarkness, a rope is pulled above the *chiqueros;* the heavy metal bolt on the *toril* gate slides open. The crowd is silent. The closed circle has been broken.

Into the arena a black bull charges and stands in the sun. The *toril* gate slams shut and again the circle is closed.

Enclosed, separated from the herd, the bull is alert. He moves, stops, turns his head. It is hot. The bull breathes easily, his mouth closed, and he sniffs the dry sand. Soft whorls of black hair cover his head between the eyes and the mouth. He runs, stops again, and raises his head. The horns are held high. The horns can lift a horse, kill a tiger, catch a leaf.

The bull stands quietly, but an infinite sense of potency exists within him and is communicated to the crowd. The power to breed is increased by the power to kill. Antonio Romero searches for the elements that will permit him to dominate the power and the horns, to create the faena and kill the bull. The challenge is immediate.

For centuries, in Spain, the bull, descended from the prehistoric wild bull of Europe and Asia, has been protected from domestication, has been chosen, bred, preserved in his original state with pleasure and with purpose. He has been given respect and honor, worshiped and feared. The existence of the bull in the arena re-creates the challenge to primitive man in ritual form.

Primeval, unreasoning, secure within his power and his horns, the bull will charge. An instinctive attack can be controlled. A series of attacks can be accepted and composed into the formal elements demanded by man to give meaning to the bullfight. The bull will oppose the form with death. The matador must create within the struggle and discipline his fear. From the rigid opposition the man will rise or be defeated.

The power and the horns cannot be given time to break from instinct into knowledge. Wounded, deceived, the bull will move from attack to defense and the danger will increase greatly. The bull will kill with certainty. Bred for the moment the bull must die. With dignity and strength the bull stands alone, as Antonio Romero observes him.

A banderillero steps from behind the barrera and swirls his cape in the air. From a distance, the bull attacks instantly. The banderillero retreats behind the barrera, allowing the planks to take the bull's assault. The horns bite into the chipped red planks and the bull backs away.

Across the ring, José Vito runs on the sand and accepts the bull's charge. He flings his cape wide with one hand. The bull follows the motion. He is deceived. The movement is repeated. The bull charges, hooks with his left horn, turns quickly.

Antonio Romero has not moved from the *burladero.* His attention is sharply directed on the bull. Behind the entrance to the arena, two picadors can be seen, mounted, ready.

The cape is flung. The bull charges, hooks left, twists, turns suddenly, charges the banderillero. The cape is flung again. He accepts the motion of the cloth hesitatingly. His attention is never wholly on the object. The banderillero is expertly running the bull, and yet, he has already been forced to take the defense. Antonio Romero continues to stand behind the *burladero.* Someone in the crowd whistles insultingly.

The bull charges, changes direction, avoids the cape. José Vito is forced to run to the barrera. Another banderillero runs across the sand and draws the bull away. The bull attacks, drives, wrenching his massive body in an attempt to destroy. The crowd applauds the bull.

The banderillero is driven to the barrera. He jumps to safety, the horns missing his body. The bull turns, runs to the center of the empty ring. His head is held high. A derisive cry is hurled from the stands at Antonio Romero.

The matador orders the banderillero to run the bull again, and a second cry is heard.

A blare of trumpets and a drum roll sound. The picadors enter the ring.

The matador has not moved since the bull entered the arena. A rising protest can be heard from the stands, urging the matador into the arena.

Antonio Romero disregards the crowd. He concentrates on the bull. With his cape, Vito runs the bull in the direction indicated by the matador. The picadors are circling the ring. The crowd is angry; they sense that they have been cheated, that the matador is not working with the bull because he is afraid to accept the bull's unbroken power. They ignore the immense difficulties a bull presents if the matador hopes to create a series of passes, a series founded upon beauty and mastery rather than an appeal to the crowd's appetite for excitement.

Antonio Romero steps from behind the *burladero* onto the sand. He walks slowly toward the bull, extends his cape. He has chosen the terrain on which he will meet the bull. The matador is standing, his feet together, the cape gathered. He moves the cloth, cites the bull.

The bull attacks. The cape is swung wide, slowly unfurling its color before the horns, guiding the bull's mass past the man's body, tempering the charge. The horns are low, at a distance from the man's body. The danger is not apparent. The control is perfect. The crowd is silent except for a few whistles.

Three times Antonio Romero draws the bull past his body in a wide circle, dominating the bull, forcing the bull to follow the cloth. As the bull exits from the encounter Antonio Romero is careful to give him an object to follow and room in which to turn. The crowd is angry; he has not brought the horns near his body. The matador wrenches the cloth from the bull's sight. The bull twists his body, tearing, tiring his body, as he searches for the cape. The bull has been brought under control by the matador. In the stands, the old aficionados are moved by the performance and applaud. Their applause is drowned by insults and cries.

Having subdued the bull's first chaotic impulse to run and charge, having fixed the bull in the exact position he desires, Antonio Romero stands, cites the bull.

The bull charges. The matador moves with precision, extends his right leg, opens the cape, and brings the bull close to his body. The horns are lowered to kill. The cape guides the horns cleanly in an arc from left to right. The horns pass within reach of the man, but the man does not move. The cloth opens. With immense power and speed, the horns are raised instantly into the air. Antonio Romero has accepted the attack. The crowd is silent.

The matador has not only met the danger; holding the horns close to him he has given the bull every advantage and has increased the danger. Antonio Romero is aware of the silence that surrounds him. The cape is drawn away. The bull turns.

The matador has judged the bull. He is aware that each time he brings the bull by, the bull gains ground and the horns stab closer. The first verónica was created with this knowledge. The second and third passes are based upon the first, with assurance and the realization that the bull cannot be given a fourth pass without obliging the man to give ground or be wounded. Antonio Romero has not rested upon chance. He has observed with perception, acted with skill and courage.

Antonio Romero guides the bull with his cape. The horns are close. The matador cuts the cape sharply away from the bull's vision. The cloth swirls around the man. The bull attempts to follow and is unable to turn within his own length. The bull is stopped, the encounter broken. His back to the bull, Antonio Romero walks toward the barrera.

The ease with which he has performed, the absence of any clear indication of danger, have left the crowd unmoved. Antonio Romero has dominated the bull; he has not made a superficial display of his mastery. But the crowd is unaware of the distinction and angry at the indifference to their demands which they sense in him. There is a division of opinion in the stands. The majority express their resentment, the few aficionados applaud.

Antonio Romero stands with Francisco Jiménez and Manolo Ortega to the left of the picador. A vicious insult is shrieked at Romero. The crowd laughs at the words and at the man who must accept them. Romero looks up with contempt.

His power unbroken, the bull attacks the picadors. Speed and power strike with a violent impact. The horse is thrown. The picador falls. Antonio Romero makes the *quite*. Taking the bull from the picador, the matador holds the bull's attention with his cape while the picador is helped onto his horse, his armored leg thrust into the armored stirrup. Antonio Romero leads the bull accurately. Making no attempt to create another series of passes, he places the bull for the second pic and walks to the side.

The crowd's anger mounts. In his attempt to

bridge the distance between himself and the crowd, the matador has given his finest and failed. His desire is gone.

"Fuera, get out, *fuera!"* A voice yells demanding the matador leave the arena. *"Fuera,"* another voice repeats. *"Fuera, fuera!"*

The pic pierces the bull's thick shoulder muscles. The picador bears down heavily. The horns search to penetrate and hold. The bull is strong, insists under the pic, and raises the horse on his horns. The crowd applauds the power of the bull. Holding the horse high, the bull pauses for an instant, braces his rear legs, renews his power. The horse and man are hurled backward onto the sand. The crowd applauds. The bull charges the fallen horse. Under the horse and mattress, the picador struggles to become free. The horns rip and tear into the mattress. The horse writhes under the weight and power, legs flailing the air in awkward fear. The bull charges, turns, charges, turns. The horse is rolled over, freeing the picador. Antonio Romero, Francisco Jiménez, Manolo Ortega and the banderilleros fling their pink-and-yellow capes at the bull, to draw the bull away from the fallen man.

The *monosabios* help the picador to his feet. The bull charges. The *monosabios* jump the barrera. The picador is left standing, helpless to run in his heavy armor. The bull's head is lowered. Francisco Jiménez throws his cape between the horns and the picador. The bull is confused.

The picador moves heavily to the barrera. Francisco Jiménez turns toward the *callejón.* His sword handler gives him a second cape. The bull charges. The matador catches the bull in the folds of the cloth and leads the bull away. He performs a series of passes which the public receives with applause. Yellow and gold whirl with the cloth and the bull. The line is quick and confused. The bull charges. Jiménez is ready to accept the horns. His legs move and carry him away from the horns. His movements change in accord with the bull's attack and the cape swirls away and out. The crowd is aroused. The terrain in which Francisco Jiménez has met the bull has changed with each pass. The matador has neither made the decision nor held it. The bull has imposed his power. Francisco Jiménez has escaped death, and the danger has been apparent to the crowd. They are moved and answer with an ovation. Francisco Jiménez looks up and accepts the applause.

The bull receives the third pic. The bull's power is still great. It must be tempered to permit Antonio Romero to create the faena the public will demand. The picador has placed the pic correctly in the center of the *morillo* and is bearing down steadily. Along the bull's straining flanks a thin flow of blood runs and drops on the sand. The bull's power is being broken in the formal manner dictated by the bullfight. The punishment is not excessive; it is being measured in relation to the bull's power. Antonio Romero stands in a line with Francisco Jiménez and Manolo Ortega. The picador holds his horse quietly and resists the bull's attack.

The public becomes angry. They shriek at the picador, demanding that the bull be spared further punishment, ignorant of the fact that if their demand is carried out the bull's power will forbid the faena they hope to see. The President exhibits a white handkerchief, acquiescing to the public's demand. The trumpets announce the banderillas. The President has not judged the bull correctly. Another pic is necessary.

Antonio Romero nods to his picador. The picador twists into the open wound. With his horse, he cuts off the bull's escape and insists with the pic. The crowd is furious. Manolo Ortega is ready to make the *quite.* In defiance of the regulations, the picador continues to punish the bull. Antonio Romero knows that the bull's power has been well broken. The picador looks at his matador. Antonio Romero does not answer. The picador widens the wound, bleeds the bull, twists the pic beyond the guard, searching for the backbone, destroying the bull. The crowd is yelling. The matador has ordered the rules broken and has openly defied the public. He has permitted his picador to destroy the crowd's pleasure.

"Fuera, fuera!" The crowd is welded into a mass. Manolo Ortega attempts to cite the bull, but it is impossible for the bull to charge until he has had time to recover his strength. The bull attempts to charge and falls to his knees.

The crowd's fury increases. Manolo Ortega leaves the arena and walks into the *callejón.*

"Fuera, fuera, fuera!"

The crowd's anger rises and fills the entire Plaza de Toros. The rhythm of their fury is expressed in the slow pounding of their words. No attention is paid to the banderillas. The bullfight is forgotten.

"Fuera, fuera, fuera!"

The police chief in the *callejón* alerts his captains, and throughout the Plaza there is a display of armed authority. The mass of fury, exasperated because it can find no physical expression, is sustained and grows.

In the *callejón* the toreros ignore the crowd. Manolo Ortega rests his arms on the barrera. Francisco Jiménez rinses his mouth out with water. The banderillas have been placed. The bull is bleeding profusely. His mouth is open. The power is broken and the bull will not charge. His breathing is heavy and labored.

Antonio Romero walks across the sand, and the crowd's rage increases. The matador stands below the President's balcony, removes his montera, raises it high, bows and requests permission to kill.

He walks toward the bull, holding the muleta in his left hand, the sword in his right. The bull is bleeding. The matador stands in front of the bull. He knows that a good faena is impossible. The bull is on the defensive.

The creation of a series of passes is based upon the bull's charge. Antonio Romero attempts to force the bull. Waiting to kill if the man comes close enough, the bull is motionless.

The faena is brief, meaningless.

Antonio Romero profiles to kill. The clamor is renewed. The sword sinks into the bull. The crowd has seen nothing, has been interested in nothing, except the expression of their rage. Antonio Romero has killed well, exposing himself to the bull's right horn, giving the bull the advantage.

The dead bull is dragged from the arena to the applause of the crowd. Antonio Romero stands in the *callejón*. His sword handler wipes the blood from the sword.

The trumpets announce the second bull. Francisco Jiménez is standing in the *burladero*.

Anger gives way to expectancy. Francisco Jiménez runs across the empty arena, kneels. His cape on the ground, he faces the open *toril.* The bull charges into the sun. The matador flashes his cape from the ground into the air. The bull follows the cloth as it sweeps high to the right of the matador. The crowd acclaims Francisco Jiménez. The bull turns. Pivoting on his knees as the cape floats to the sand, the matador receives an ovation. The bull attacks. The horns catch the cloth, tearing it from the matador's hand. Francisco Jiménez is defenseless.

He runs to the barrera as his banderilleros make the *quite.* The picadors enter. The crowd is aroused. Following the first pic, Francisco Jiménez executes three awkward verónicas and the acclaim grows. Each pass is accompanied by indecision and an absence of rhythm. As the horns jab past his legs, Francisco Jiménez offers the spectacle of a man whose courage and desire to please cannot be doubted. Francisco Jiménez respects the crowd. He has made the danger clear, and the crowd is excited. Francisco Jiménez watches the bull take the second pic. The horns reach high and rip the horse's throat. Francisco Jiménez looks up at the President and orders the picador to withdraw the pic. The crowd applauds. The picador backs his horse away from the bull. The President grants the matador's request and the trumpets blow.

Antonio Romero opens his cape, steps in to make the *quite.* The crowd shrieks its scorn. Antonio Romero folds his cape, walks into the *callejón,* puts his cape over the barrera.

Francisco Jiménez' desire to spare the bull another pic has been granted. The bull's strength is intact, his wind uncut. He is fast, alert.

Manolo Ortega is standing in the *callejón,* his arms over the barrera. Jiménez' banderillero runs in an arc toward the bull. The bull attacks. The banderillas are high. Their steel barbs flash down and the bull breaks his charge, throwing off the rhythm of the man's calculated run. The banderillero twists, high in the air, to escape. Manolo Ortega jumps the barrera and runs toward him. The horns catch the banderillero. The banderillero falls and the bull charges the body on the sand. Manolo Ortega is unprotected; his cape is in the *callejón.* Francisco Jiménez and Antonio Romero run, their capes open. Manolo Ortega races between the bull and the fallen man. The horns twist. The bull is instantly drawn toward the fleeing matador. Manolo Ortega sprints to the right, away from the man on the ground. He runs in a zigzag from the charging bull. The bull, his horns lowered, gains ground. Manolo Ortega leaps the barrera.

The banderillero is helped to his feet. He is unhurt. The crowd applauds Manolo Ortega and turns its attention to Francisco Jimenez.

In the center of the ring, his montera extended in his right hand, Francisco Jiménez turns slowly and drops the montera onto the sand. The crowd applauds the dedication in its honor.

Francisco Jiménez looks at the crowd. He performs a series of manoletinas, pretending to ignore the bull, as he pivots and moves from one pass to another.

"Olé!"

The horns flash in a quickening tempo, and the crowd's devotion becomes intense.

"Olé!"

The horns stab closer, and the crowd is brought to its feet.

The bull cuts in, jolting the matador off his balance. Jiménez turns, angered by the indignity, rushes the bull, smacks the confused animal on the nose and kneels.

The power of the ovation rises. Francisco Jiménez throws his sword and muleta to the side and stares up at the bull. The ovation grows. The matador turns on his knees and offers his back to the horn. He looks up at the crowd, and lies back. The bull cannot see Francisco Jiménez.

The critics note the manner in which Jiménez is exhibiting himself. The aficionados, to whom the bullfight is a tragedy, turn away in disgust.

"Last week he bit the bull's horn."

"And he gets a fortune for this, lying on the sand sunning himself."

The confusion brought about by the six fast manoletinas is gone. The bull has caught his breath. Jiménez sits up, groping on the sand for his sword and muleta. The bull sees the movement, and, as the matador stands, he charges. Jiménez flings the cloth wide and the bull is diverted.

The crowd watches Jiménez begin a series of derechazos. The muleta is spread wide by the sword and the horns pass quickly. The bull cuts, jabs, turns, forcing Jiménez to retreat with each pass. The motion is quick, blurred. The bull hooks. Jiménez breaks away. The bull has won the terrain.

"Olé, Olé!"

In his years as a matador, Francisco Jiménez has suffered many minor wounds; he has been thrown, bumped, stepped on by the bulls. He has always given an impression of spectacular risk and has never been badly gored. It has always seemed to the crowd as if Francisco Jiménez could not escape death on the horns. His frail body and melancholy contribute to the air of personal tragedy he carries even while performing to please the crowd. There is no ease in Francisco Jiménez' movements, no assurance in his manner.

He has been forced to break the encounter with the bull. The bull is still fresh; his mouth is closed and he breathes easily. Another pic, and the bull would have been slowed down; a faena would have been possible. The bull charges straight, with speed, but there is increasing danger. The bull has learned to distinguish between the matador and the cloth.

With the muleta, Jiménez could break the bull's power, force the bull to follow. In a series of passes designed to wrench and tear he could condition the bull, cut the animal's speed, dominate. With the muleta he could confine the bull, bring the bull within his control. The crowd would observe in ignorance; the aficionados would be moved.

Francisco Jiménez runs across the arena. He stands at a great distance from the bull. He jumps, waves the muleta in his left hand, as the bull attacks. Across the arena, the bull charges. Francisco Jiménez has folded the muleta to his side.

The horns are lowered. Francisco Jiménez exposes the muleta. The horns are raised. The matador is forced backward. The bull passes him.

"Olé!" A shriek is released by the crowd.

The bull turns, charges. Jiménez whirls in a series of passes, forced by the bull to retreat. He is thrown spinning through the air. The crowd is horrified. The matador jumps to his feet, and the men who have run in for the *quite* return to the barrera. The bull attacks. The muleta is torn from his hand. The bull attacks again. Francisco Jiménez escapes behind the nearest *burladero*.

An ovation greets him.

The matador cites the bull for the kill. The bull charges. Jiménez backs away. It is impossible to focus the bull's attention on the muleta. To kill the bull correctly, by going in straight over the right horn, is to be killed by the bull. The bull has not been dominated. He is confused, cautious, strong. His head is high. The crowd watches tensely.

Four times Jiménez profiles, starts in; four times the bull charges, stops, turns to avoid the muleta, which must deceive, and accompany the sword.

Francisco Jiménez runs to the side, jabbing toward the bull in an inept and grotesque fashion. The bull turns toward the matador, attacks. The sword sinks through the neck. Strangling in his own blood, the bull sways, coughs, falls. Francisco Jiménez stands triumphantly as the bull dies.

A wave of roaring applause bursts from the crowd. They have seen a bull slaughtered and have confused a sudden death with tragedy. The classic laws of the bullfight, which exact the highest courage and skill from the matador, have been ridiculed. In return for the right to kill, the matador must offer himself. To kill with honor the matador must command.

Francisco Jiménez stands by the barrera. The stands fill with waving handkerchiefs. The President of the bullfight accords two ears to the matador in response to the overwhelming acclaim offered by the crowd. Francisco Jiménez has triumphed in his desire to please the crowd; he has failed before the challenge of the bull.

Followed by his banderilleros, Francisco Jiménez circles the arena as he receives the ovation. In a wave of enthusiasm the audience stands as the matador passes. Cigars, jackets, hats, flowers are thrown at the feet of the matador who has gratified his public. Jiménez enters the *callejón* and again comes forward to bow in answer to a last acclaim.

The *toril* gate is open. Manolo Ortega is standing in the *burladero*. His cape is raised above his eyes, pressed between his body and the planks. Manolo Ortega has never seen a bull of his enter the ring. He watches his banderillero on his left. The bull is in the arena. Manolo Ortega lowers his cape. He is eighteen and one half years old. He has killed three hundred and eighteen bulls since he was fifteen and has been wounded seven times.

The bull is slow. He charges sluggishly at the capes, avoids contact, waits for the men to commit themselves in his terrain. The bull takes up a defensive position by the *toril* gate and will not charge Manolo Ortega. Instead the bull attacks and withdraws, attacks, returns to the position he has chosen. Manolo Ortega attempts to draw the bull out. He compromises himself. The bull hooks, catches the cape on his horns, tears the cloth viciously, retreats.

The picadors enter the arena. The bull attacks, hesitates. The picador pursues the bull. The bull charges, throws the horse backward, retreats. Juan Ortega anxiously observes his brother from the *callejón*. Experience has taught him to fear the cowardly bull. The bull's actions cannot be anticipated. The attack cannot be controlled, cannot be formed. The movement is erratic. If the protagonist does not fill his role the matador cannot act. The bullfight is predicated upon the brave bull.

The crowd is aware that the bull is bad. His cowardice is obvious. The bullfight becomes a travesty as the picador follows the bull around the arena, accompanied by the toreros. The men attack the bull in a reversal of roles, urging the bull to charge. They move with caution. The horns can kill. The grotesque procession moves around the ring. The crowd is annoyed.

The bull takes two light pics that leave his power intact, and the trumpets blow.

The crowd shows discretion and does not urge the matador to place his own banderillas. Manolo Ortega's banderilleros place double-barbed black banderillas in the bull, as an indication of the bull's cowardice.

They work efficiently, avoiding the horns, showing their disrespect for the bull by placing the banderillas in the safest way possible. Manolo Ortega makes no attempt to act with honor. The bull is despised by the crowd, by the matador. The bull is the negation of the qualities a brave bull possesses. Cunning has replaced nobility. The open attack has become deceit, and the bullfight has lost its essential meaning. Only if the challenge exists can the matador create.

Manolo Ortega advances, attempting to weaken the bull, forcing the bull to the muleta. The crowd is exasperated by the farce. They have lost interest and are anxious to see the bull dead.

"Mátalo, kill it, *mátalo,"* someone yells. The cry is taken up and repeated.

From the *callejón* Juan Ortega whispers to his brother, "Watch out," and the bull attacks, hooking, jabbing with both horns. The bull retreats.

"Mátalo!"

Manolo Ortega had hoped to triumph in his first fight as a matador in this city. But he is afraid of the bull. His desire to triumph has given way to the hope that he will be able to kill the bull. The crowd will forget. They will not condemn if the bull is killed quickly, before their annoyance grows into anger.

"Mátalo!" Juan Ortega shouts to his brother. His hands are clenched on the rim of the barrera. The bull's head is high.

Manolo Ortega's banderilleros are standing near the matador, ready.

"Mátalo!"

Manolo Ortega knows he can win the crowd if he kills well, force them to accept him. The bull lowers his head, the chance is given. The matador judges the instant. He runs, crosses with the muleta. The sword sinks into the bull high between the shoulder blades. The banderilleros whirl their capes. The bull turns, twists. Manolo Ortega has killed well, and the crowd applauds. They expected, and would have excused, a bad kill.

Juan Ortega is angry. The violent tension he was under as he watched his younger brother demands relief. He insists that it was insane to attempt a good kill. Only luck saved Manolo from the horns. No control was possible. Manolo Ortega gestures toward the crowd, toward the applause in answer to his brother and steps onto the sand. The applause grows. The crowd honors the matador who has risen beyond their demands, who has shown courage and a determination to succeed.

A single turn around the arena is accorded Manolo Ortega by the crowd.

It is 6:35. Three bulls are dead.

The shadow cast by the Plaza de Toros has lengthened. Antonio Romero stands in the *burladero*. The *toril* gate is opened.

The crowd is prepared to issue its demands. Romero's desire to give is limited by his contempt for the crowd. As Vito runs the bull, Antonio Romero observes. The crowd's anger is not forgotten. Abruptly the matador runs toward the bull, his cape extended. Vito withdraws. In this bull, Antonio Romero has seen the qualities that can be formed into a classic faena, not the faena composed of fifty flashing passes, the matador trusting to God and luck, which moves the crowd, but the faena Antonio Romero knows to be the best.

Antonio Romero guides the bull with his cape. The bull's strength is judged. The picadors cut the power in answer to the matador's command. Underneath the powerful charge Antonio Romero senses an intelligence which is being awakened. The matador acts with decision. His movements and those given the cape are conceived with care. No action exists without its reason. The bull, the power, the horns, the intent to kill are worked and molded with knowledge. A constant balance is maintained between the bull, the man and the cape.

Antonio Romero orders the manner in which the banderillas are placed. His men work quickly. Antonio Romero is focused upon the bull. He is aware of the bull's changing condition.

His thoughts are directed toward a single aim, to kill the bull. To kill the bull in the manner that exacts the utmost courage.

Antonio Romero dedicates the death of the bull to a friend. The matador walks across the sand, holding the muleta close to his body in his left hand. He stands, gives the bull the muleta, brings the bull past in a slow, curved line. His left arm is extended. The bull turns.

Bringing the horns past his chest, Antonio Romero extends the line. Regulating the rhythm, Antonio Romero creates a unity between himself and the bull. He carves a series of statues in motion, the red draped cloth serving to bind the man and the bull together.

Antonio Romero ignores the existence of the crowd. He feels neither contempt nor interest, nor a desire to give. He is absorbed in his work, in the bull, in the form he has given the bull. He is sensitive only to the bull. The terrain Antonio Romero has chosen to command is held.

The bull charges and gives dimension to the line drawn by the muleta. In sharp opposition to the fixed stance taken by the matador, the black mass of the bull moves against a line of purple and gold. Antonio Romero has committed himself. He stands directly in line with the horns. The bull is obliged to change the trajectory of his attack. Between Antonio Romero and the horns there exists only the control given the muleta by the wrist and the knowledge upon which the control is based.

The muleta is in the left hand. With each pass, the bull is shown the direction in which the cloth moves, the direction which the cloth will be given at the moment of death.

To kill the bull, a moment in time must be chosen, a moment in which Antonio Romero will offer himself to the bull, a time in which the man's life will depend upon his courage and skill. To kill the bull, receiving the attack, the matador must be secure in the knowledge that the bull will obey the muleta. Antonio Romero calculates the number of passes the bull can be given; too many and the bull will learn to distinguish between the muleta and the man, too few and the matador cannot rely on the bull to follow the cloth at the moment of death. The fierce discipline that is being imposed on the bull must not be broken. The attack must be maintained. If the bull retreats into defense, the matador cannot kill receiving the horns.

The faena has existed for three minutes. In the stands the aficionados are in awe. Reluctantly the crowd has forgotten its anger. Each pass is joined to a mounting cry.

"Olé, Olé, Olé!"

The word is torn from the crowd. For an instant a universal rhythm is created between the bull, the matador and the crowd. The bull charges, the muleta guides the horns. *"Olé,"* the bull, the muleta, *"Olé,"* the bull, the muleta, *"Olé."*

Antonio Romero stands profiled to the bull. He has chosen the moment to kill. He stands erect, the muleta in his left hand, the sword held in a line with his right eye. The bull's attention is fixed on the muleta.

Antonio Romero moves the muleta gently. The bull attacks. Antonio Romero stands directly in the line of the attack. He is receiving the bull. The horns are lowered. The muleta crosses to the right of the matador. The horns follow the muleta. Antonio Romero extends his right arm. The motion is slow, protracting the infinite danger. The horns are below the matador's body. The sword penetrates the bull. The muleta guides the horns to the right, away from the man. The sword sinks into the bull. The bull raises his head. The horns stab into the muleta. Antonio Romero has not changed his position. He steps to the left, and the encounter is broken. Antonio Romero, matador de toros, has killed the Conde de la Corte bull with as much honor as any man has ever killed.

A retired matador who has not fought in thirty years is crying in the stands.

The bull staggers. In giving death to the bull, Antonio Romero has increased in stature, has created and given. He has offered himself to the horns and he has controlled the horns. He has opposed his knowledge and courage to the bull's power.

The bull falls, struggling in death. Antonio Romero stands.

The crowd is divided. The kill came when the majority were hoping, demanding, more, more, more passes. If the matador had complied, if he had not ignored the mass, instead of tragedy there would merely have been a display of speed and luck. The kill was executed perfectly, before the crowd was granted its unspoken demand.

The bull is dead. Their heads uncovered, in respect to the bull, the men accompanying the team of mules run across the sand, attach the horns of the dead bull, crack their whips, drag the bull from the arena. The crowd stands and applauds the bull.

The opinion of the crowd is divided between wonder and anger, between applause and insults. Antonio Romero is standing in the *callejón*, his head down.

White handkerchiefs are waving in the stands. The *alguacil* approaches the barrera holding a single ear cut from the bull, granted to the matador by the crowd, by the President of the bullfight. Antonio Romero remains in the *callejón*. The applause increases. The *alguacil* offers the ear to the matador. The matador refuses.

In the stands an aficionado turns in rage to a friend. "Antonio is right. If the Jiménez faena was worth two ears, Antonio should get the whole bull. This should not be." And the man stands to applaud and offer his devotion to Antonio Romero.

The *alguacil* holds the ear up. The matador refuses. He is urged through the *burladero* by a friend. He accepts the ear, and as the insults mount beside the applause, throws the ear to the ground, bows to the applause and walks into the *callejón*. His sword handler gives the matador a handkerchief and Antonio Romero wipes his eyes. He stands looking at the cement floor of the *callejón*. A friend walks over to Antonio Romero, puts his arm around the matador's shoulders and says, "They are not worth it, Antonio."

The crowd is watching the *toril* gate. Francisco Jiménez is standing in the *burladero*.

He composes a series of flashing figures which brings an immediate response from the crowd. He is applauded during the first *quite*.

The banderillas are placed. The matador rinses his mouth with water. He starts the faena standing with feet together, raising the muleta with both hands to permit the bull to run past him. His eyes close involuntarily with each pass. The horns stab past his thin legs.

Francisco Jiménez turns toward the stands, passes the bull to the right, while looking over his left shoulder at the crowd in seeming disdain for the bull. The pass is repeated. Francisco Jiménez is met with an ovation. He smiles at the crowd.

"Olé!"

Changing the muleta to his left hand, the matador brings the bull by in rhythm to the muleta.

"Olé!"

The second pass causes Francisco Jiménez to step back.

The bull charges. Francisco Jiménez is pierced by the bull's right horn. The rhythm is destroyed. The horn penetrates; yellow and gold are spun through the air. The man twists on the horn. Francisco Jiménez is flung. His body falls to the sand. The bull attacks, horns low.

Toreros surround the bull, struggling to draw the horns away with their capes. In the confusion of motion the bull stands over the fallen matador refusing the capes. Antonio Romero throws his cape over the bull's eyes, hoping to blind him to the man who lies wounded on the sand. The bull tosses the cape from his eyes. Juan Ortega, who has joined the others, grabs the fallen cape. The bull hooks, tears Juan Ortega's shirt and throws him to the ground. Juan Ortega runs.

Francisco Jiménez lies free of the bull. He is carried from the arena into the infirmary. The crowd releases a murmur of anguish.

Antonio Romero has forced the bull to his cape, and now holds his attention. Manolo Ortega, in white and gold, gathers his cape together. Antonio Romero walks toward the barrera, and Manolo Ortega holds the bull. In the *callejón,* Juan Ortega brushes the sand from his eyes and tucks his torn shirt into his trousers.

The crowd stirs. Mouths anxious with fear repeat questions.

Francisco Jiménez lies naked on the operating table.

Antonio Romero exchanges his cape for the muleta and sword. He cites the bull. Manolo Ortega walks to the barrera. Antonio Romero cuts the bull into position, profiles to kill. The sword penetrates, strikes bone and is flung into the air. Antonio Romero is handed a second sword. He profiles. The sword plunges into the bull. The banderilleros spin the bull with their capes. The sword works within the bull's body.

Antonio Romero places the muleta under the bull's muzzle. The bull is dying. In his right hand the matador holds a sword high above the bull's lowered head and brings the point to within inches of the base of the skull. The bull attacks, tears the muleta from the matador's hand and forces the men back. The matador escapes the horns. The bull sways. The *coup de grâce* is attempted a second time. The bull's mouth hangs open; he is breathing deeply, exhaling blood. The bull's legs are braced apart to hold up his body. He staggers. Antonio Romero moves with caution near the horns. The bull rips the cape of the banderillero standing beside the matador, and charges. The banderillero loses his balance, falls. The horns reach him. The bull staggers and is dead. Antonio Romero turns toward the *burladero*.

Manolo Ortega steps into the *burladero*, and the sixth bull runs into the circle. The crowd is silent. Its attention remains focused on Francisco Jiménez.

Across the arena, the bull charges the banderillero's cape. The man escapes behind the barrera and the bull breaks his run. The horns rip upward and the thick red planks are snapped and thrown into the air. The circle is broken. The bull runs toward the center of the arena.

High among the cheap seats, the last light of the sun shines in the eyes of the crowd. The heat has grown less. The whole arena is in the shade.

In the infirmary, Francisco Jiménez is being given a blood transfusion. Tossed on a stool in a corner of the operating room the matador's clothing lies torn. Yellow and gold are stained with the blood of the bull, stained with the blood of Francisco Jiménez.

"Olé."

Manolo Ortega brings the horns past his body.

"Olé."

It is 7:15.

The cape flows in a perfect rhythm.

"Olé."

The matador pivots. The bull thrusts his horns high, tearing the cape from the matador's hands. Twisting quickly, the bull catches him. The boy falls, rolls, and does not move. Antonio Romero makes the *quite*. Manolo Ortega lies face down on the sand. The bull charges the picador.

Manolo Ortega stands, walks to the *callejón*. He sits on a pile of capes, throws his head back and gasps. The matador's sword handler pours water over the boy's head. Juan Ortega borrows a fan from a woman in the first row and fans his brother. The boy lies back, shudders. The wound in his thigh is minor. The white silk absorbs the blood. Manolo Ortega is faint from shock. He stands, grabs a cape and walks toward the *burladero*. Juan Ortega holds his brother back, trying to prevent him from entering the arena. Manolo Ortega breaks loose, violently shouting at his men, at his brother. He enters the circle. The crowd applauds.

Manolo Ortega creates a series of chicuelinas. His cape flowing in a graceful line, the boy spins, the horns stab. The strength and the mass of the bull are twisted into a figure that describes a circle round the boy in white.

"Olé."

The line is clean. The bull charges straight. The attack is met with elegance.

"Olé!"

The trumpets sound.

Manolo Ortega goes to the barrera.

"Matador, Matador, Matador!" The crowd chants its demand.

Manolo Ortega takes the banderillas from the ring attendant. His left thigh is bleeding. The matador's banderilleros stand at the edge of the barrera. Manolo Ortega waves them out of the ring. They do not move.

"*Fuera*, get out," he yells at them. The men leave the circle, and the boy and the bull are alone together.

Manolo Ortega breaks into a fast run. The bull attacks. The boy cuts sharply, in front of the bull; his arms are held high; his body flashes up, arms together, high. Down, into the bull, the banderillas stab and the boy twists away from the horns through the air.

"Olé."

Four times the boy spins in the air, straight, in rhythm with the bull's attack. Four times he runs to meet the bull; four times the banderillas stab together. The crowd stands.

"Olé!"

Manolo Ortega receives an ovation.

The matador dedicates the death of the bull to the crowd. He walks slowly toward the bull. His left leg twists and he stops to keep from falling; his face contorts with pain. Antonio Romero runs toward him. The older matador tries to help him from the arena. The boy fights back, shouting, "Leave me alone. Get out!"

The crowd is silent. Manolo Ortega walks toward the bull. He is in pain. The bull attacks.

The boy raises the muleta. The horns attack; the bull turns; the boy turns; the unbroken rhythm moves and quickens the crowd.

Stretching forward on his right knee, his left leg extended in support of his body, Manolo Ortega cuts the cloth from horn to horn. The bull responds, hooking at the cloth, wrenching his neck and body in answer to the muleta. Manolo Ortega is exhausting himself in an attempt to meet the challenge.

He stands within a foot of the bull. The punishment inflicted by the muleta has dominated the bull.

The bull retreats. The matador is forced to advance into the bull's terrain. Manolo Ortega offers his body, the muleta hidden behind his legs. The bull attacks and is deceived by the muleta. Slowly and with infinite care and danger the bull is drawn from his chosen terrain toward the center of the ring.

Juan Ortega watches his brother with apprehension.

Changing smoothly from the punishing passes, the boy extends the muleta in his left hand. His legs are set wide apart, his weight equally distributed so as to forbid retreat. There is no hesitancy. The wrist guides the bull. The bull turns in an arc. Manolo Ortega's banderilleros are crouched, prepared to run with their capes.

The bull stops midway through the attack. The horns are low, opposite the boy. The wrist stops. The muleta hangs still. The horns turn toward Manolo Ortega. The Plaza de Toros is silent.

The boy moves the muleta. The bull's attention shifts to the cloth. If the bull is permitted to hesitate longer the command will be broken. The horns turn, their black tips almost touching the cloth. The matador is obliged to complete the pass. He must extend the line begun by the muleta and confirm his control. In the extension lies the danger that the bull will not obey, will not be deceived by the cloth, and will wound the matador.

Manolo Ortega is forced to risk the act. He has chosen to place himself beyond retreat. He stands on the sand, legs apart, his left hand holding the muleta to his side, his right arm behind his back holding the sword in a direct line with his left leg.

Manolo Ortega is compelled to remain motionless; to move is to attract the horns, to be caught; only the muleta will direct the bull's charge away from the matador.

Manolo Ortega prolongs the pass. The bull attacks the muleta.

In the Plaza de Toros the released tension becomes a cry.

The matador draws the bull toward the barrera. He is intent upon offering proof of his control. As he walks, the boy's left leg collapses repeatedly, forcing him to stop. In anger, Manolo Ortega strikes his foot on the ground to straighten his leg. The pain is increasing.

Manolo Ortega extends the muleta between his body and the barrera.

"No!" the crowd shrieks.

The bull attacks.

"No!"

There is no exit for the bull except the one indicated by the boy. The bull is obliged to pass between the barrera and Manolo Ortega. Three times the matador commands the bull to charge within the narrow confines imposed by his decision.

The crowd is silent. The limits imposed upon the bull constrict the crowd's expression.

The bull is released from the encounter.

The crowd stands.

Manoletinas, fast and in a tight circle, join the matador and the bull in a quickening rhythm. The bull attacks. The muleta moves up and back, up and back, forming a single flowing line. The speed increases and is maintained, in a series of derechazos.

The crowd is undivided. The critics, the aficionados, the ignorant are joined within the rhythm created by the matador and the bull.

Manolo Ortega has dominated the bull and the crowd. He stands, sights along the sword. The crowd is silent at the moment of death.

The muleta crosses. The bull attacks. The sword hits bone. The right horn catches Manolo Ortega and hurls him twisting through the air. Antonio Romero makes the *quite*. The boy falls, stands, staggers, falls again, stands shouting at Antonio Romero, at the banderilleros who have run to his side, who have taken his bull away with their capes.

"*Déjalo!* Leave him!"

Manolo Ortega profiles. He runs straight toward the horn. The sword hits bone. The right horn throws the figure in white and gold awkwardly into the air. The figure falls and lies still. The *quite* is made. Helped to his feet, the boy staggers, shocked, toward the bull, pushing the toreros away as they try to carry him into the *callejón*.

The light is dim in the Plaza de Toros. Behind the mountains the sun has set.

It is 7:30.

A third time the sword hits bone, and Manolo

Ortega is seen grotesquely twisting, falling, grasping for his muleta and sword on the sand, again standing before the bull.

The crowd is silent.

A fourth time Manolo Ortega throws himself upon the bull's right horn. The sword penetrates the bull. The bull staggers.

Manolo Ortega stands, his right arm held high above his head. The bull falls. Manolo Ortega hears the crowd. He turns, collapses upon the sand. The bull dies.

Antonio Romero and the boy's sword handler carry Manolo Ortega into the infirmary.

The stands fill with waving white handkerchiefs, announcing the crowd's favor, expressing its devotion to Manolo Ortega's honor. The President concedes the ears and the tail of the bull to the matador. Juan Ortega receives the symbols of his brother's triumph from the *alguacil.*

Manolo Ortega lies on the operating table, naked from the waist down. Through the grilled window high on the wall above, the boy can hear the crowd's acclaim. The surgeon is cleaning the wound, drawing the silk and gold thread from the torn flesh.

Juan Ortega runs past the police on guard outside the infirmary, into the operating room. He hands the ears and the tail of the bull to his brother. Manolo Ortega sits up, holding his trophies in both hands.

Francisco Jiménez' agony has been dulled with an anesthetic. Penetrating the inner surface of the right thigh adjacent to the knee the horn has taken an upward trajectory, lacerating muscle, tearing the sciatic nerve, entering the abdomen and causing intestinal evisceration. The horn has perforated the bladder, torn the femoral vein, causing intense hemorrhage with traumatic shock. The surgeons explore to determine the further extent of his injuries.

The matador's manager sits on a stool in a corner of the room. The cuadrilla stands in silence.

Outside the infirmary a dense throng is waiting anxiously.

Antonio Romero is told that Francisco Jiménez' condition is critical. Later tonight, on the road, Antonio Romero will listen to the radio and learn whether Francisco Jiménez is expected to live.

Manolo Ortega is ordered to lie still. He raises his head, afraid that the surgeon will forbid him to appear tomorrow at the bullfight in Alicante. The matador is assured that he will be able to travel tonight, that he will fight tomorrow.

It is 7:40.

Across Spain the bullfights are over.

In the east, Emilio Posada and Carlos Huerta are resting in the hotel. Emilio Posada cut one ear this afternoon and has lost his terror. He has asked his manager to get him a contract to fight in Barcelona at the end of the month.

Carlos Huerta is receiving friends in his room. His sword handler is packing. The matador is leaving in an hour. Tomorrow Carlos Huerta will appear in Alicante with Antonio Romero and Manolo Ortega.

The bulls from the ranch of Don Juan Pedro Domecq are in the corrals behind the Plaza de Toros in Alicante.

ABONOS MIRA

101A

101B

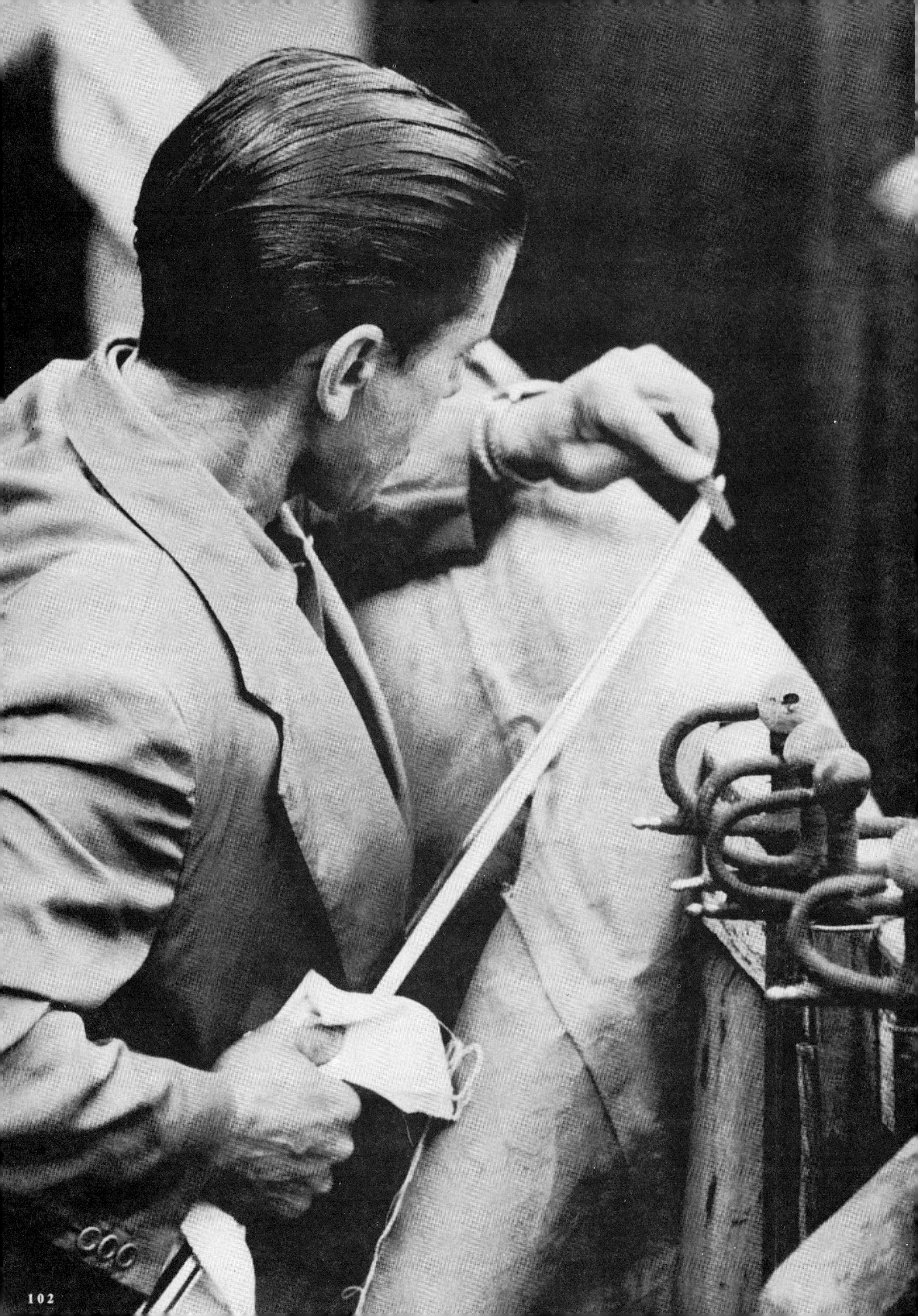

103A

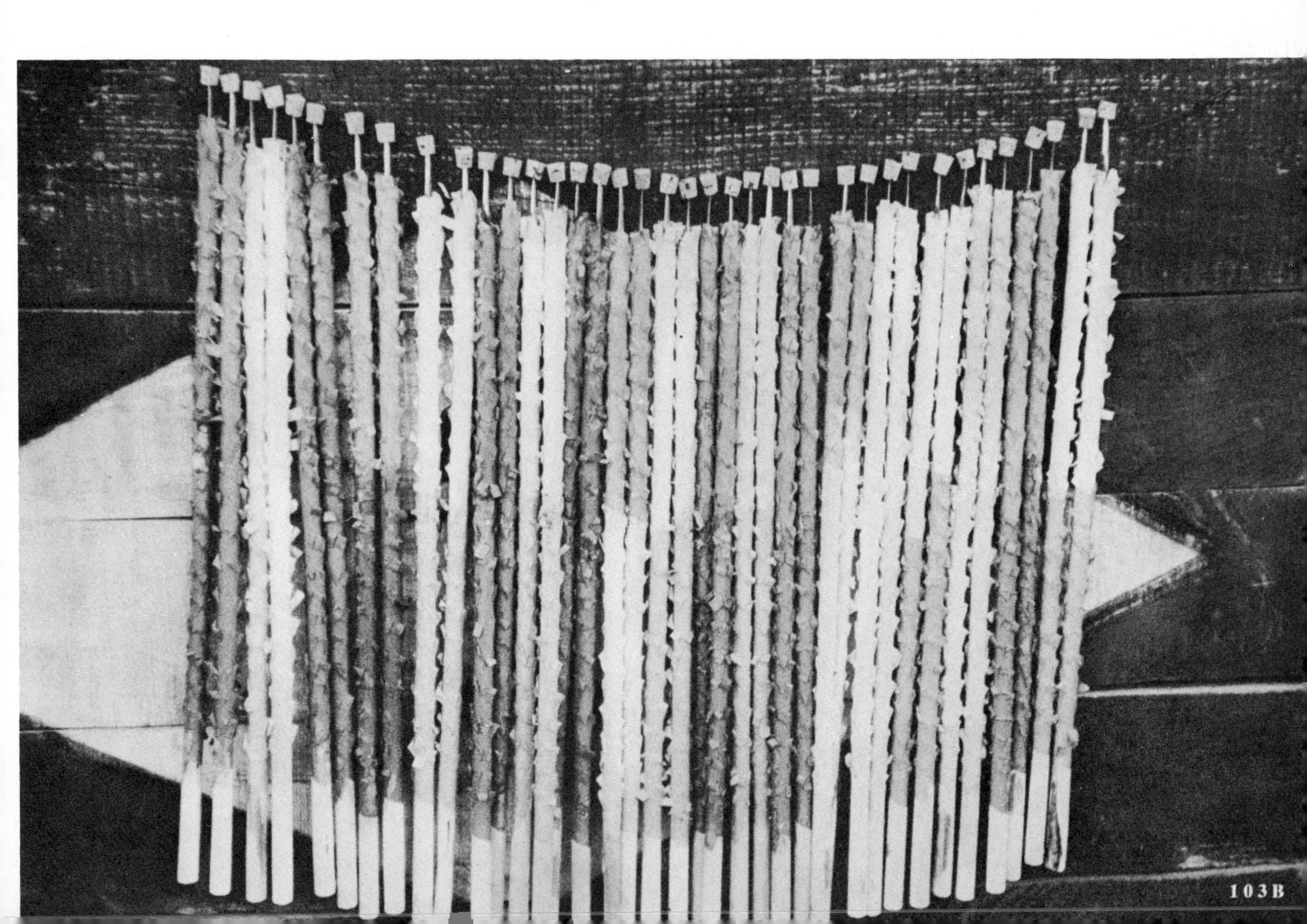

103B

116A

116B

PICADOR

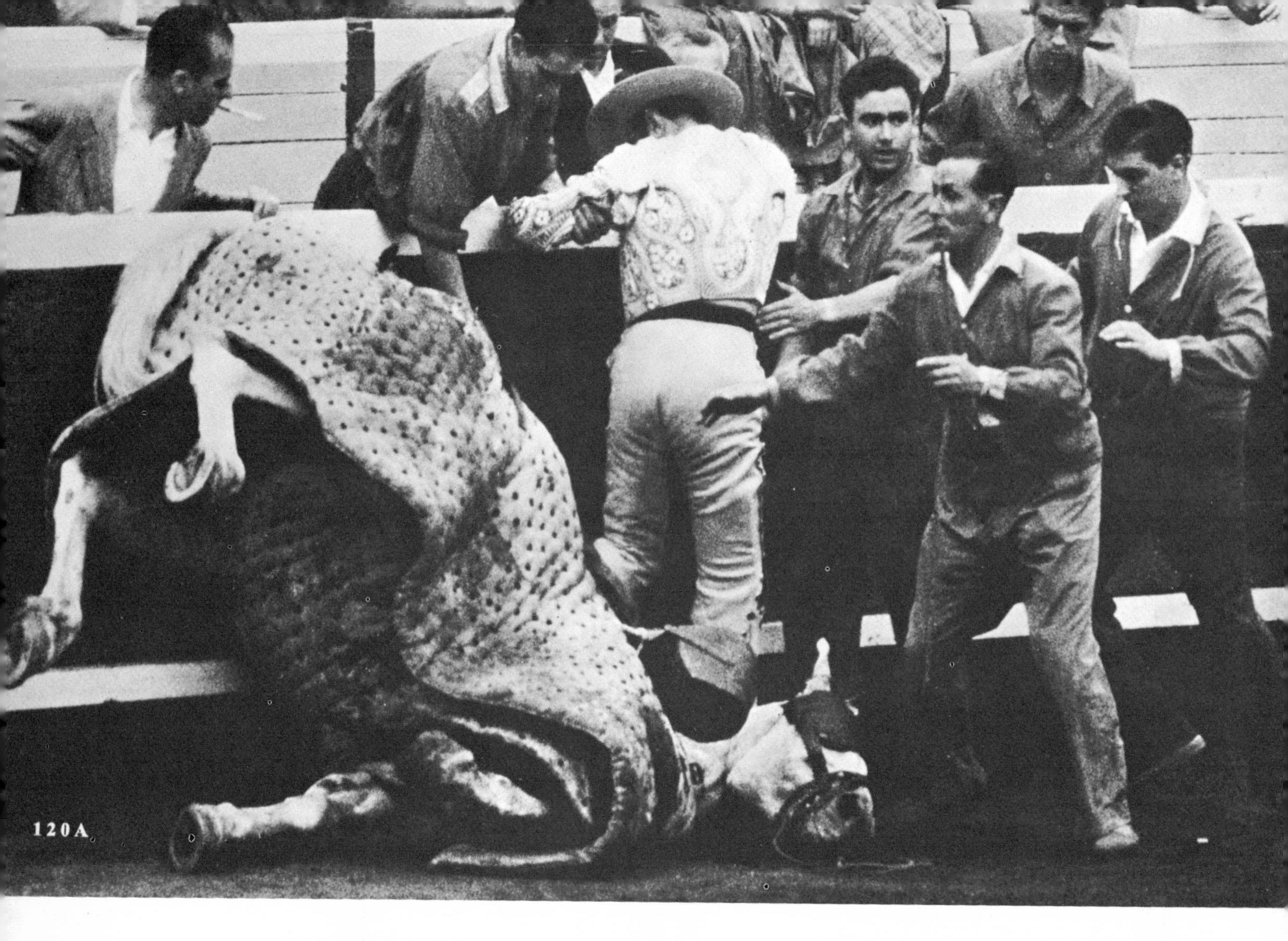
120A

120B

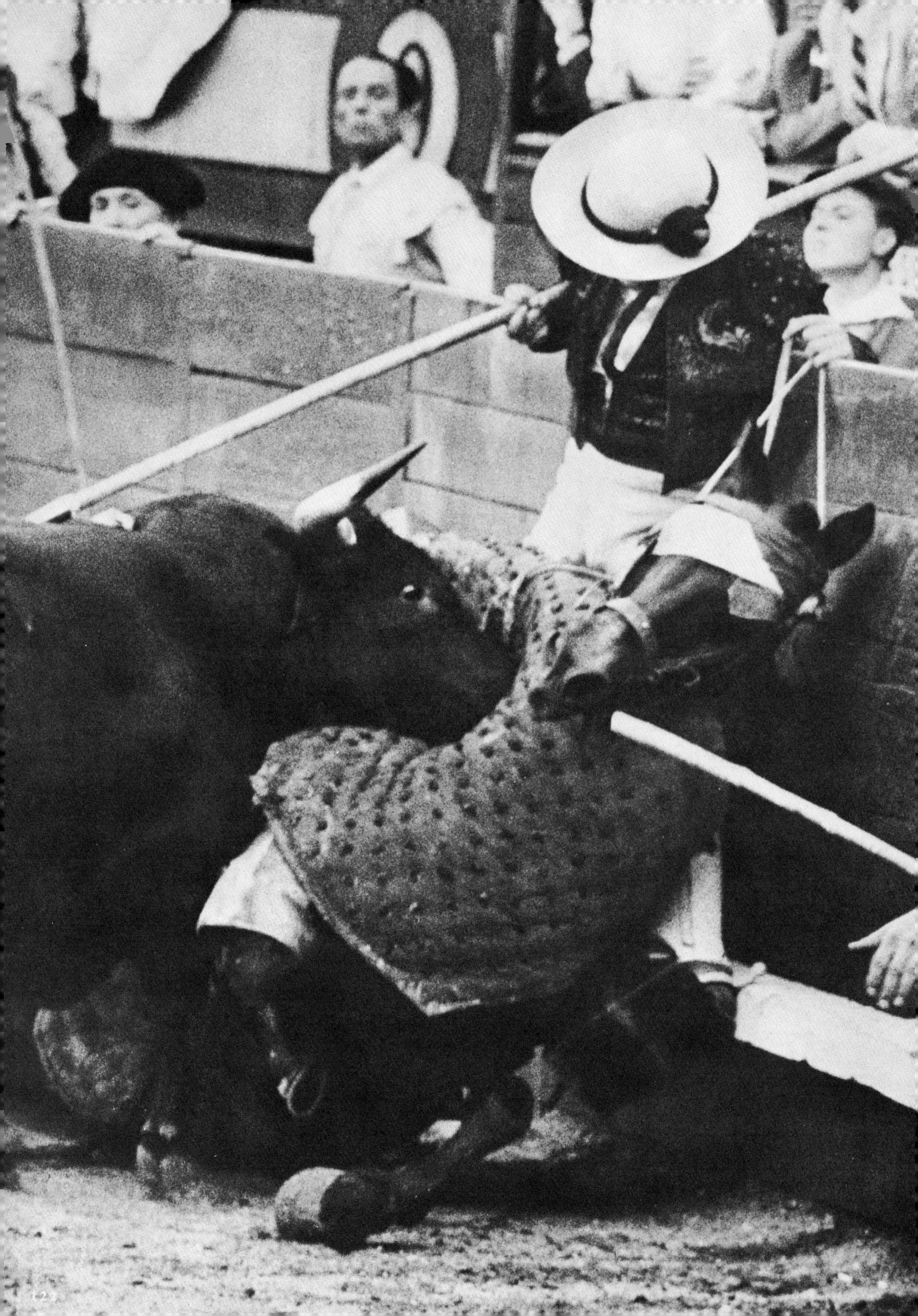

BANDERILLERO

MATADOR

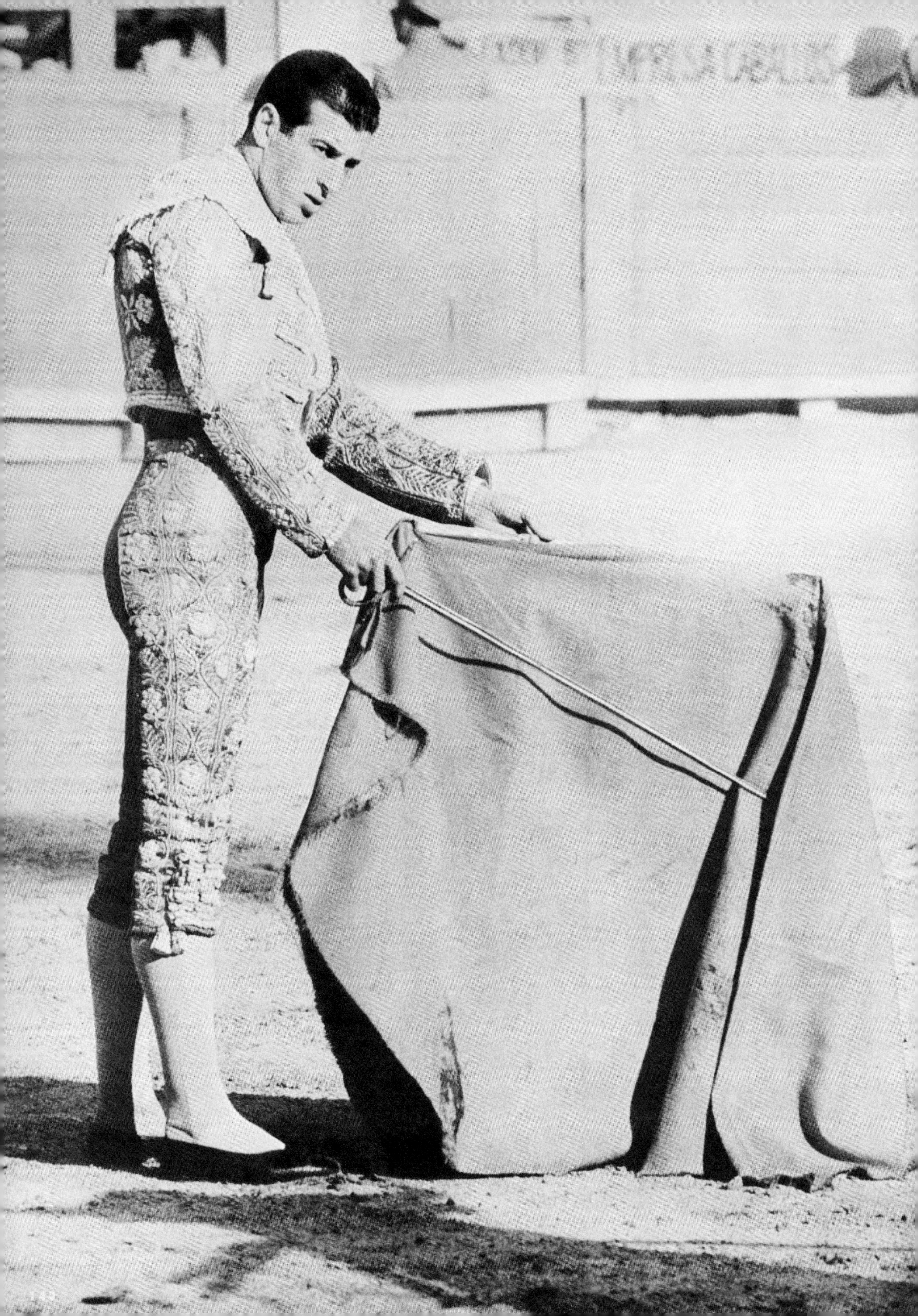
EMPRESA CABALLOS

ARENEROS

2

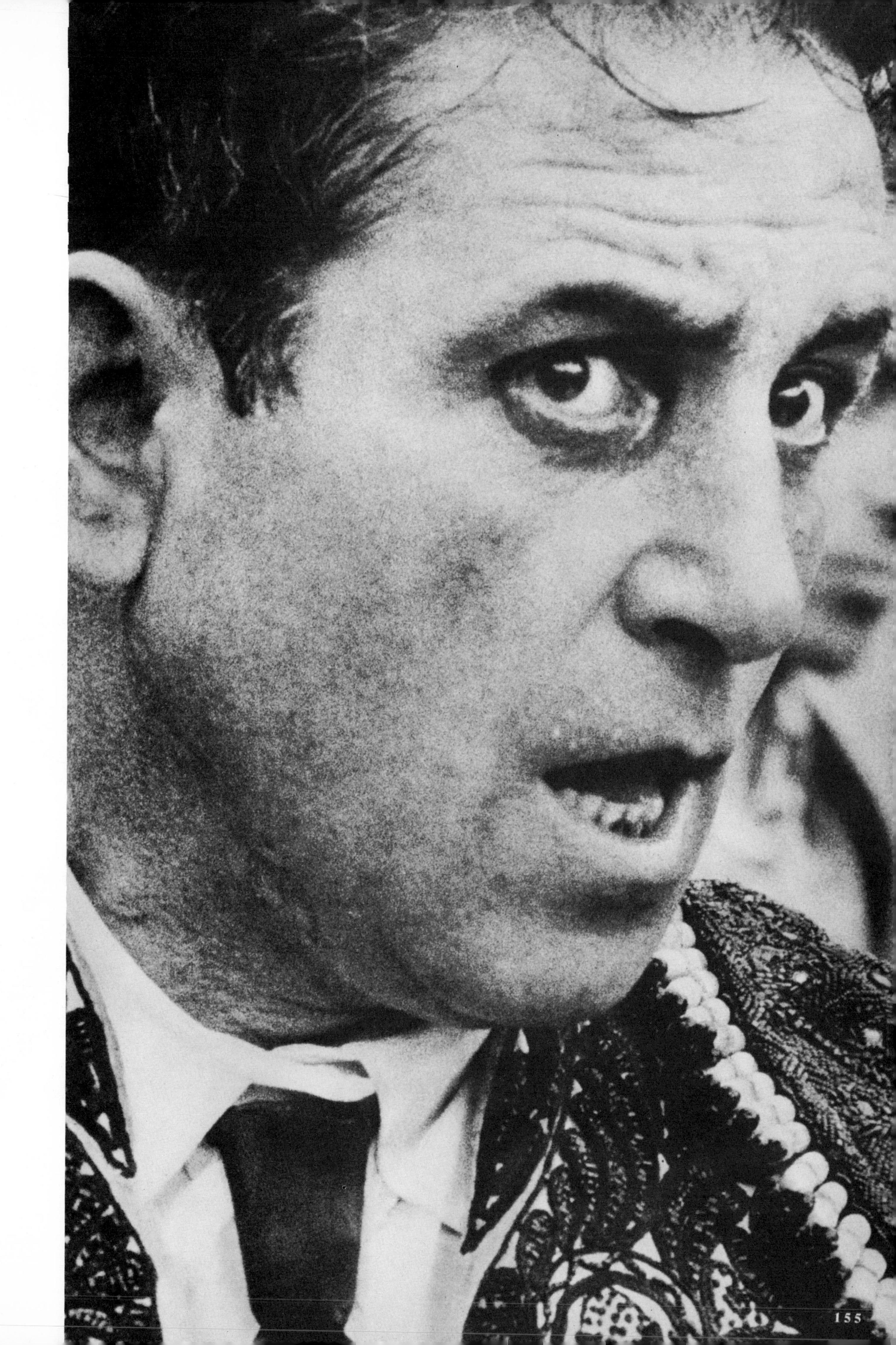

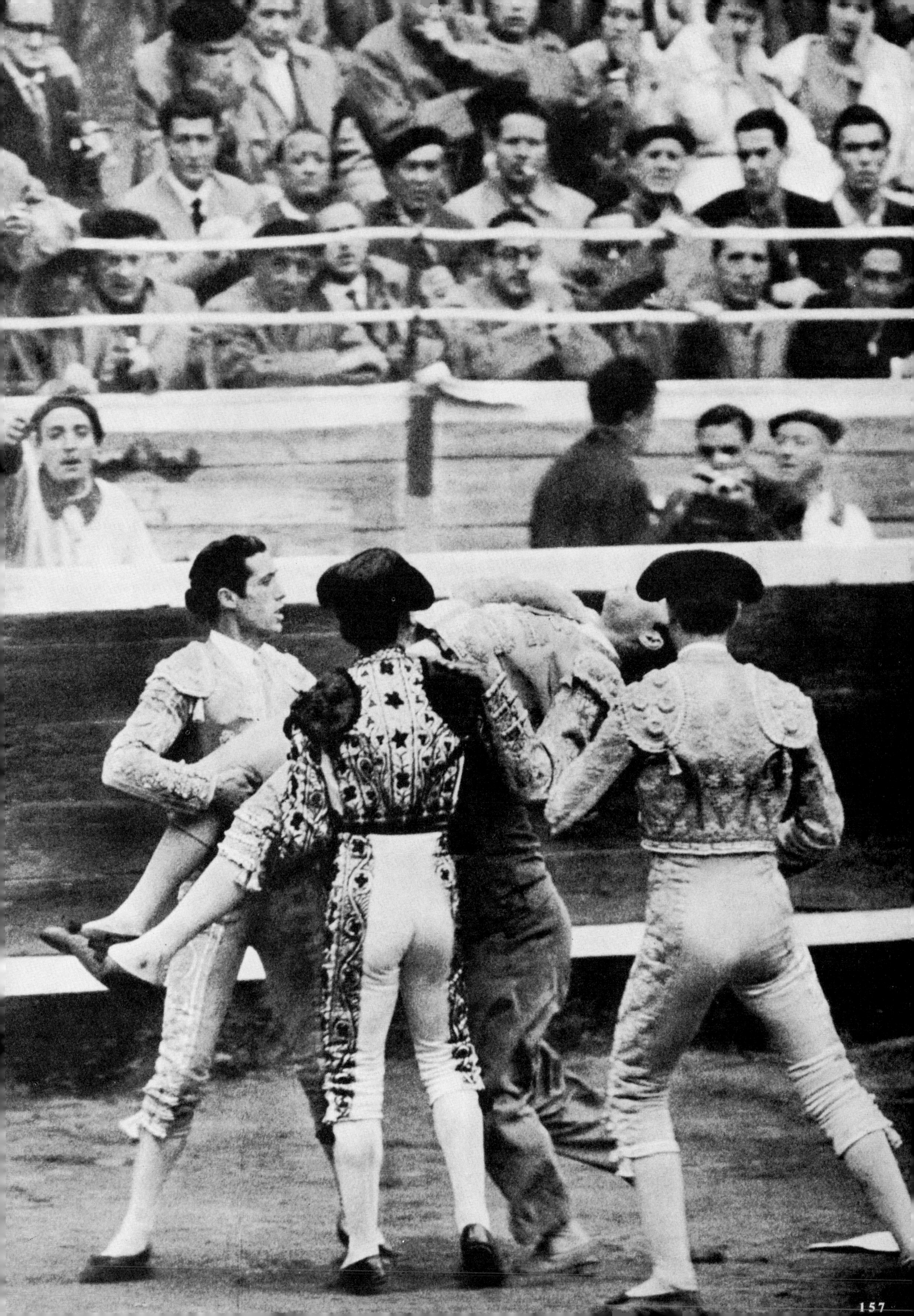

ENFERMERIA
SE PROHIBE el PASO

162A

162B

1

KILL

ALFA
EBRO
ORTEGA

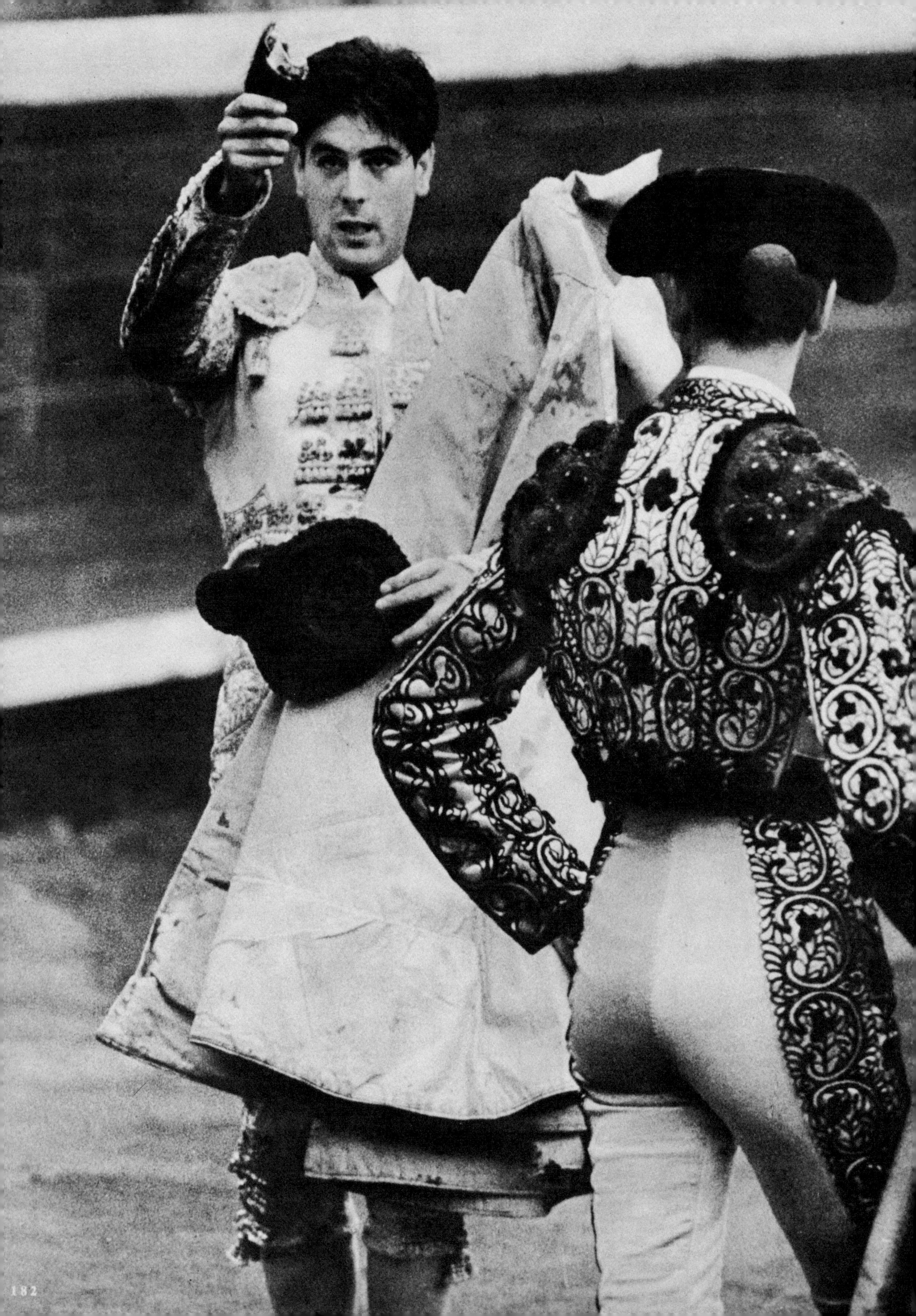

Picture Captions

2 Natural pass; the bull charging. Bilbao
19 Cuadrilla's car. Driver is packing luggage on the roof. Aranjuez
20a Plaza de Toros. Málaga
20b Bull entering corridor which leads to the chiqueros. Behind the wooden protective walls are men who work the ropes controlling the gates. Valencia
21 Lobby of Gran Hotel, Salamanca, an hour before the bullfight
22 Alternativa ceremony, Barcelona, September 1957. César Girón, matador, gives the alternativa to his younger brother, Curro Girón.
23 Manuel Jiménez ("Chicuelo II"), matador, being carried by the crowd from the bull ring to his hotel. Málaga
24a Crowd during feria. Sevilla
24b Parade masks. Pamplona
33 Twelve-year-old boy in bullfight school. Valencia
34 Twelve-year-old boy in bullfight school, working with his older brother as the bull. Valencia
35 Crowd in Chinchón before the bullfight. The men at the bottom are in the ring and will leave when the fight begins. Above them the crowd is watching from the balconies of the houses surrounding the town square which has been turned into a bull ring.
36a Young becerristas waiting for the paseo. Alicante
36b Bull ring in the town square. Chinchón
53 Corridor surrounding the corrals. Plaza de Toros, Málaga
54 Conde de la Corte bulls in the corral. Plaza de Toros, Málaga
56 Patio between the corrals and the bull ring at noon while the apartado is taking place. Málaga
57 Sorteo. Granada
58 Bull separated from the others during the apartado. Salamanca
59 César Girón outlines a pass while dressing for the bullfight. Hotel Excelsior, Valencia
60 César Girón praying. Hotel Miramar, Málaga
93 Entering the arena; the poles are pics. Valencia
94 Crowd. Valencia
96 The matadors Miguel Báez ("Litri"), Antonio Bienvenida, Antonio Ordóñez and their banderilleros getting ready for the paseo. Valladolid
97 Antonio Ordóñez, "Litri," and banderilleros bowing to the President of the bullfight. On the right, the sword handlers are holding the capotes for which the matadors are about to exchange their ornate capotes de paseo. Valladolid
98 Paseo. Salamanca
100 Millán Borque, critic for the Madrid newspaper *Informaciones,* sitting at the barrera. Logroño
101a Don Alipio Pérez, ganadero who breeds bulls near Salamanca, sitting at the barrera. Salamanca
101b Two mayorals who have accompanied the bulls from the ranch. Bilbao
102 "Miguelín," Antonio Ordóñez' sword handler, sharpening the swordpoint. Bilbao
103a Picador; the pics are in their racks. Toledo
103b Banderillas, their points protected with corks, hanging from their barbs in the callejón. Cuenca
104 Domingo Ortega, matador (right), talking to a friend. Valencia
106 Matador's capote de paseo in front of the barrera seats. The crowd is buying soft drinks and sandwiches from a vendor in the callejón before the bullfight starts. Valencia
107 Alguacil. Valencia
108 Gregorio Sánchez, matador, holding the capote and running toward the bull. San Sebastián
109 Bull charging into the arena
110 Antonio Borrero ("Chamaco"), matador: verónica. Barcelona
111 Capote pass toward the back. Madrid
112 Antonio Ordóñez: verónica. Sevilla
114 Luis Miguel Dominguín, matador: larga cambiada on his knees. Bayonne
115 Media verónica. Bilbao
116a Rafael Girón, matador: media verónica. Barcelona
116b Domingo Ortega: *quite*. Valencia
117 Picador
118 The bull lifts the horse.
119 The horse is thrown.

120a Under the effect of morphine, the horse does not struggle and will remain in this position until the monosabios and areneros put him on his feet again. The horse is not wounded.
120b Domingo Ortega on the day he came out of retirement in 1953 at the age of 48. Valencia
121 Picador. Bilbao
122 Picador. Córdoba
123 Banderillero. Albacete
124 Banderillero seen by the bull. Madrid
125 Luis Miguel Dominguín citing the bull. Valladolid
126 Banderillero citing the bull. The matador with the cape is ready to make the *quite*. Valencia
128 The banderillas stab down. Linares
129 Julio Vito, banderillero de confianza in "Litri's" cuadrilla. Albacete
130 César Girón. The banderillas are straight and close together, as they should be. The bull is charging fast, and the man is directly in a line with the horns. Córdoba
131 Twisting in the air away from the horns. Bilbao
132 Twisting away. Segovia
133 "Litri"
134 Antonio Ordóñez requesting permission from the President to kill the bull. Málaga
135 Jorge Aguilar, matador, dedicating his bull to a friend. Valencia
136 The crowd. Salamanca
137 César Girón, ready for the faena, walking toward the bull.
138 Bull
140 Antonio Ordóñez citing the bull. Almería
141 "Litri," the bull, the crowd. Valencia
142 Manolo Vásquez: natural pass. Santander
143 Enrique Orive, novillero: natural pass. Bilbao
144 Curro Girón: natural pass. Linares
145 Manuel Jiménez ("Chicuelo II"): natural pass. The bull has thrust the muleta high. Granada
146 Antonio Ordóñez punishing the bull with the muleta. Bilbao
147 Antonio Ordóñez forcing the bull to return for a second pass in a series. Bilbao
148 César Girón: pase de pecho. Zaragoza
150 Antonio Ordóñez: *ayudado por alto*. Bilbao
151 Antonio Ordóñez: *ayudado por alto*. Bilbao
152 Antonio Borrero ("Chamaco"): derechazo. It is said that the finger of Chamaco's left hand is pointed toward heaven for inspiration. Bilbao
153 César Girón: derechazo. Aranjuez
154 Luis Miguel Dominguín: natural pass. Zaragoza
155 Picador
156 Manolo Vásquez, matador, caught while attempting a natural pass. The sword is still in his hand; the muleta can be seen flying through the air. The horn has penetrated his left thigh and is entering the abdomen. This wound was very serious and caused Manolo Vásquez to miss half of the 1956 season in Spain. Valencia
157 Antonio Borrero ("Chamaco") being carried from the ring. He was wounded in the abdomen. Bilbao
158 Door to the infirmary. Salamanca
159 Matador, wounded in the groin, being carried from the ring. Aranjuez
160 The bull. Zaragoza
161 "Litri": *ayudado por alto*. His eyes close involuntarily. Burgos
162a Julio Aparicio, matador, punishing the bull with short chopping passes
162b Matador tiring the bull by forcing him to stop short. San Sebastián
163 Curro Girón. Pamplona
164 "Litri": afarolado. Bilbao
165 César Girón: manoletina. Pamplona
166 Manuel Jiménez ("Chicuelo II"): derechazo. Pamplona
167 Gregorio Sánchez: manoletina. Bilbao
168 Manuel Jiménez ("Chicuelo II"): pase de pecho. Málaga
169 César Girón on the day he was badly wounded. Burgos
170 Calerito, matador, going in to kill. Valencia
171 Juan Montero, matador, going in to kill. Albacete
172 Antonio Ordóñez going in to kill. Palencia
173 Rafael Pedrosa, matador, striking bone with the sword. Bilbao
174 Gregorio Sánchez: the sword is all the way in. Bilbao
175 "Litri" killing. Valencia
176 César Girón killing, the sword in to the hilt. San Sebastián
177 César Girón killing, the sword in. Pamplona
178 Antonio Ordóñez watching the bull die. Málaga
180 Matador circling the ring and receiving an ovation from the crowd. Bilbao
182 Jaime Ostos, matador. Having cut an ear, he stands to receive the crowd's acclaim. Zaragoza
183 The dead bull's horns are attached to the traces of a mule team which will drag the bull from the arena. Bilbao
184 Sixteen-year-old seed bull on a ranch in Andalucía.

A Note on the Photography

THE PHOTOGRAPHS in this book were taken over a seven-year period in Spain, the majority during the 1956 season from June to November.

Almost without exception the photographs in the arena were shot with a 300-mm. f/4 Sonnar telephoto lens mounted on a 35-mm. reflex camera body. I chose this lens not only to eliminate the distance between camera and subject but also to isolate the subject from the area surrounding it. To increase this isolation and to heighten the fact that the matador is alone with the bull, I used a wide opening on the telephoto lens; the resulting shallow depth of field throws the background very much out of focus. The high magnification, 6X, of the 300-mm. lens helped me to select details which I otherwise could not have seen.

Tripods are forbidden in the stands, where they would annoy the spectators, and in the *callejón*, where they would interfere with the movement of the toreros. Consequently the 300-mm. lens was hand held. Until I became familiar with the equipment, I had the lens and camera mounted on a gun stock, and I used an 18-inch cable release to trigger the shutter.

Tri-X film, which I rated at 650 A.S.A., was used for all photographs taken in the shade. Under the changing light conditions of the bullfight, this allowed a shutter speed of 1/200 second at f/4 at the end, when the light is dim, compared to 1/500 second at f/6.3 at the start, when there is intense reflected light in the shade.

For sunlit areas, or when a shutter speed slower than 1/200 second was suitable for the action in the shade, I used Plus-X film rated at 200 A.S.A. In the sunlight speeds ranged from 1/200 second at f/18 to 1/500 second at f/8.

These figures serve as an indication of the extreme light conditions to be found at the bullfight in Spain. A light meter was always used and checked every twenty minutes.

In addition to the 300-mm. lens mounted on the reflex camera body, I used a series of lenses—28 mm., 35 mm., 50 mm., 85 mm., and 135 mm.—with two Leica M-3 cameras. One of the Leicas was always set for the sun, the other for the shade.

Glossary

Abono: Season ticket for the bullfights in a particular city, or a group of tickets for a specified number of bullfights at feria time.

Aficionado: Fan, amateur, one who likes bullfights. Used properly to designate the person who understands the technique and nature of the bullfight.

Alternativa: The official ceremony that promotes the novillero to the rank of matador de toros. If the alternativa takes place in the provinces, it must be confirmed by repetition in Madrid. An alternativa given in Mexico City is recognized in Spain. After the banderillas are placed in the first bull, the trumpets announce the faena. The senior matador gives his muleta and sword to the novillero, who then faces his first mature bull. The second matador on the cartel acts as a witness to the ceremony. The new matador returns the muleta and sword to the senior matador in a repetition of the ceremony before the death of the second bull. The matadors then act in the order of seniority. This ceremony used to be performed among picadors and banderilleros but is no longer observed by them. No rules exist concerning the length of time a man must be a novillero before he receives the alternativa. For many years the alternativa has been accorded with increasing indulgence. Novilleros with little knowledge of the bulls and of techniques are often promoted to the rank of matador solely for the object of being able to command higher fees.

Alguacil: The representative of the President of the bullfight. He remains in the *callejón* and transmits the orders of the President to the toreros.

Apartado: The act of moving the bulls from the open corral into their individual pens underneath the bull ring. The *apartado* by custom takes place at noon on the day of the bullfight. The aficionado attends it for two reasons: to enjoy seeing the bulls and to study them in order to be able to estimate the afternoon's fight.

Arenero: Bull-ring servant who smooths the sand of the arena before and after the death of each bull. The word "arena" means sand in Spanish.

Arrucina: A rarely performed, extremely dangerous

pass invented by the Mexican matador Carlos Arruza. Man and cloth form one target. The muleta and sword are held in back of the matador in the right hand, and the bull is offered a very small target of cloth which protrudes from behind the left knee. If the bull has a tendency to hook to the left, the matador will be wounded when attempting this pass.

Banderilla: Wooden stick, one inch in diameter, twenty-eight inches long, decorated with colored paper. The banderilla is armed at one end with a two-inch, barbed steel harpoon. The banderillas are placed in pairs, as close together as possible, high on the huge tossing muscle behind the bull's neck. The banderillas serve to wound and tire the tossing muscles so that the bull will have a tendency to keep his head low when the matador goes in for the kill.

Banderillero: One who places the banderillas. There are three banderilleros in a cuadrilla. The banderillero intervenes with his cape under the orders of the matador and according to the necessities of the fight. He is paid by the matador and belongs to a union. Banderilleros are often former novilleros without the courage and talent necessary to become a matador. A good banderillero can make a steady income for a long time. Today there is a fine banderillero in one matador's cuadrilla who is 63 years old.

Banderillero de confianza: The best and most experienced banderillero in a cuadrilla. He appears at the *apartado* and, with the banderilleros de confianza of the other matadors, draws lots for the pair of bulls his matador will fight. Afterward he also reports to his matador on his impression of bulls.

Barrera: Heavy wooden fence, usually red, which encloses the arena. The word barrera also refers to the first row of seats in the stands.

Becerrada: Fight in which *becerros* are killed and in which the picador does not appear. *Becerradas* take place in most villages of Spain. There is a comic element to the *becerrada* because of the smallness of the bull and the great fear and awkwardness frequently displayed by the local toreros.

Becerrista: One who fights and kills bulls under three years of age.

Becerro: Correctly applied to denote any bull under three years of age, but generally used in reference to a bull between one and two years old. In practice a *becerro* is a bull too small or too young to be fought in a novillada.

Belmonte, Juan: Matador de toros (1892–). Retired in 1935 after appearing in 750 corridas in which he killed 1,550 bulls. A great and courageous matador whose presence in the ring revolutionized the art of bullfighting. Don Juan is today a breeder of bulls.

Bombita: Nickname used by Emilio Torres (1874–1947) and his younger brother, Ricardo Torres (1879–1936). Both were fine matadors.

Bronca: The noise made by the crowd to show their anger—combination of hooting, whistling, yelling, stamping, insults—accompanied, if the police are not looking, by throwing.

Burladero: A shelter, placed inside the ring in front of an opening in the barrera. The *burladero* is the same height as the barrera and is placed some fourteen inches away from the barrera, permitting a man to slip sideways behind it. There are usually four *burladeros* and they are marked so as to be immediately visible to the toreros in the ring.

Callejón: Corridor between the barrera and the base of the stands, about five feet wide, used as the wings of a stage: a place from which to exit into the arena and from which banderillas, capotes, muleta and sword, glass of water, towel are handed to the toreros.

Capote: Cape, pink on the outside and yellow on the inside, between 42 and 47 inches long, according to the size of the torero. Used by banderilleros and matadors. Serves the purpose of drawing the bull's attention so that the man holding it will be able to move the bull according to the necessities of the fight, i.e., place the bull before the picador, place the bull in proper position for the banderillero, draw the bull away from a fallen torero. The capote is used by the banderilleros at the beginning of the fight as an object for the bull to charge, permitting the matador to study the individual tactics of the bull he must kill. The capote is a functional tool in the hands of the banderillero. It is subject to artistic rules only when it is used by the matador. Because of its size, the capote is more difficult to handle than the muleta, but, as it offers the bull a larger target, the protection for the man is greater.

Capote de paseo: Silk cape worn only during the opening procession. It is richly decorated with gold or silver and embroidered in vivid colors, most often representing flowers and/or religious scenes. The *capote de paseo* is placed over the railing in front of the first row of seats immediately after the procession.

Cartel: Poster announcing the bullfight. Used also to refer to the program of a bullfight, i.e., the matadors and the bulls who are to appear. Cartel also means the degree of popularity the bullfighter has: i.e., "He has a great cartel in Salamanca but not much in Toledo."

Chicuelina: Pass made with the capote invented by the matador "Chicuelo," (Manuel Jiménez Moreno), born in 1902. The man offers the capote to the bull, holding it level with his chest. As the horns pass, the matador spins in the direction opposite to the bull's charge, wrapping the capote about his body. He then stands ready to repeat the pass.

Chiquero: Pen underneath the bull ring in which the

bull is isolated during the afternoon between the *apartado* and the fight. When it is time for the bull to appear in the arena the door to the *chiquero* is swung open by a rope from above.

Cogida: Tossing of a torero by a bull; it does not necessarily imply the existence of an open wound (*cornada*).

Coleta: Short braided pigtail which used to be worn by toreros as a sign of their profession. Today the torero wears a fake coleta which is clipped onto the hair at the back of his head.

Cornada: Penetrating wound made by the bull's horn. Most *cornadas* are given between the groin and the knee because at the instant when the horns pass the man the bull's head is lowered; therefore, if he hooks, he will catch the man in this region. The particularly disastrous aspect of a *cornada* is that there is usually more than one wound: a man caught in the upper inner thigh may be swung into the air on the horn with tremendous force, and in the air his weight, together with the tossing of the bull's head, will spin him on the horn, which will tear in many trajectories. The time that elapses between the instant when the man is on his feet to the penetration of the horn is about 1/25 of a second. In the past, a matador might die from infection two months after a *cornada;* today, because of advances in medicine, *cornadas* are less frequently fatal, and if the matador is alive two days after the *cornada* he will undoubtedly live. A Spanish maxim says that the blood which is lost with the first *cornada* is the blood of courage. Often you cannot truly judge a man's courage until after his first serious wound.

Corrida: Bullfight. A ritual tragedy in which the bull is killed. The corrida has a rigid form into which the bull must be made to fit. The essential element to this form is the bull's death and it is precisely this which gives meaning to the entire drama.

Cuadrilla: The banderilleros and picadors under the orders and pay of a matador. There are two picadors and three banderilleros in a cuadrilla.

Derechazo: Classic pass made with the muleta held in the right hand, the cloth being extended by the sword, which never leaves the right hand. The enlarged muleta gives the derechazo less merit than the natural, which is made with the left hand and in which the cloth offers a smaller target to the bull. The derechazo is one of the three basic muleta passes in the repertory. (See: *Natural, Pase de pecho.*) Derechazo is also used to denote any pass made with the right hand.

Dominio: Mastery, domination, control. Defines the authority and power which the matador displays in his work and which can be achieved only if he possesses a great knowledge of the bulls.

Faena: Work. In bullfighting it refers to the work done with the muleta by the matador, i.e., the entire series of passes made with one bull.

Farol: Pass made with the capote. The cloth is offered to the bull, and, as the bull passes, the matador raises the cape above his head and spins in an opposite direction to the pass taken by the bull. For an instant the matador's back is to the bull, and as the pass is completed the matador is again facing the bull.

Feria: Series of bullfights in a particular city.

Ganadero: Breeder of animals. In bullfighting, a breeder of bulls. Formerly the *ganadero* was a nobleman who raised bulls purely for the sake of raising them. He not only picked the bulls for the ring but decided in what order they would appear. Nowadays the important managers visit the ranches and choose their own bulls, and the banderilleros draw lots to determine the pair for each matador. Raising bulls has become more and more a commercial enterprise.

"Guerrita": Rafael Guerra (1862–1941), matador de toros. Great matador from Córdoba. Retired in 1899. His appearance in the ring marked one of the important epochs in the history of bullfighting. His name on the cartel assured the public of at least one good performance.

Gonzales, Manolo: Matador de toros born in Sevilla in 1929. Retired in 1953.

Guapa: Handsome, good-looking, gay, daring. *Guapo,* the masculine form, means love-maker, gallant, beau. A compliment to a man or a woman.

Guardia civil: National police of Spain.

"Joselito": José Gomez Ortega, matador de toros (1895–1920). Born in the province of Sevilla at Gelvez. Son and brother of famous matadors, he began his fabulous career at the age of twelve and became one of the truly great matadors in history. When he was killed by the bull "Bailador" at Talavera de la Reina May 6, 1920, all of Spain went into mourning. Joselito was a great friend, companion and rival of Juan Belmonte. Tall, graceful, courageous and intelligent, Joselito combined an intuition and an encyclopedic knowledge of the bulls with a virtuosity which has never been surpassed.

Larga: Pass made with the cape held in either hand, in which the cloth is flung wide and high to one side. Done on the knees for spectacular effect when the bull first enters the arena. Facing the bull, the cape on the ground before him, the matador swirls the cape; the bull usually leaps after the cloth. Luis Miguel Dominguín does this some twenty-five feet directly in front of the *toril* gate.

Machote: Colloquial for *macho*. Vigorous, robust, male; part of an instrument which enters into another.

Sledge hammer, screw-pin. Applied to a man of great courage and virility.

"Manolete": Manuel Rodriguez Sanchez (1917–1947). Born in Córdoba. One of the great figures in bullfighting, Manolete was killed by the bull "Islero" in Linares on August 28, 1947. His death was a national tragedy.

Manoletina: Muleta pass used by Manolete, but, despite its name, not invented by him. A right-hand pass in which a corner of the muleta is held from behind in the left hand. The cloth is raised above the horns as the bull passes and the matador turns on the spot in a direction opposite to the bull's path. A pass enjoyed by the public, even though it is not particularly dangerous as practiced by most matadors. A ridiculous trick of some matadors, of looking into the stands and not at the bull as they perform the manoletina, has come into vogue.

Matador: Killer of bulls.

Mayoral: Foreman on a bull ranch. He is responsible for the branding, breeding, herding, feeding and watering of the bulls and of shipping them to the plaza de toros. The *mayoral* is also in charge of the corrals at the bull ring.

Mazzantini, Luis: Matador de toros (1856–1926). Mazzantini's faenas with the muleta were poor, his cape work mediocre, but he was probably the finest killer in the history of bullfighting, the finest matador in the true sense of the word. Many hundreds of times Mazzantini killed slowly, prolonging the infinite danger, in a straight line and with an honesty rarely seen. His place on the list of the great matadors reposes upon his merit as a killer.

Media Verónica: (See: Verónica).

Miedo: Fear.

Monosabio: Wise monkey—*mono* (monkey), *sabio* (wise). The assistants on foot who aid the picador, sometimes direct his horse, help the picador to mount, raise a fallen horse.

Montera: Head covering, worn by all toreros on foot. Black, thick, and rather heavy, the montera extends in a bulge on either side of the head, giving it a strange shape. The montera is always removed by the matador before the faena and is handed or tossed to the person to whom the matador dedicates the death of the bull. If the bull is to be dedicated to the public, the montera is dropped on the sand after being raised high in a gesture toward the stands.

Muleta: Red, heart-shaped woolen cloth used by the matador during the faena in preparation for the kill. A stick, twenty-one inches long, permits the matador to hold the muleta in one hand, at the same time giving dimension to the cloth. The pointed end of the stick is placed through the center of the muleta, which is then allowed to fall in a fold upon itself. A screw is placed through the cloth itself into the other end, securing the muleta to the stick. The development of the role played by the muleta is synonymous with the history of the bullfight. Originally any cloth served the man on foot in his attempt to protect himself, to deceive the bull. The muleta is often referred to as an *engaño*: lure, deceit, fraud, mistake. To oblige the bull to charge the cloth is to *engañar* (verb): to deceive, fool, hoax, cheat the bull away from his true target, the matador.

Until this century the muleta was primarily a functional tool. By forcing the bull to attempt a turn in a space shorter than his own length, chopping the muleta from one eye to the other, suddenly withdrawing the muleta from the bull's vision during the charge, the matador could tire and wound the bull in a series of frantic lunges which tore the muscles. The muleta was also used to correct faults in the bull's charge which could prove fatal to the matador at the moment of the kill. Until fifty years ago the matador stood upon his merit as a killer far more than he does today.

With Juan Belmonte the muleta began to acquire the role of an instrument of artistic expression in itself. Though the original functional role remains, it is often ignored by today's phenomenon in his attempt to construct a series of passes, standing inches from the horns, in a faena which may last ten minutes. The public demands more and more passes, and yet, if a bull enters the arena with whom it is impossible to create forty passes, the public becomes furious at the matador. An impasse has been reached which can be avoided only by an educated public able to choose between its conflicting desires. If the public insists on a prolonged faena, then younger, smaller, less powerful bulls must be accepted; if older bulls are to appear in the arena (instead of the four- and even three-and-a-half-year-olds which are seen today and which should appear only in the novillada), then the emphasis will have to be once again on the kill instead of the faena.

Some rules which govern the use of the muleta:

1. All passes must be made in accord with the characteristics of the individual bull.
2. Passes must be created in series.
3. Passes must be made within the narrowly restricted terrain chosen by the matador.
4. The terrain must be held during the series.
5. The bull should be shaped in such a manner that the kill can be properly executed: cut or preserve the bull's strength, correct dangerous tendencies to hook with either horn.
6. The bull must be dominated, in the sense that the bull must be forced to obey the muleta.
7. Rhythm must be maintained between man and bull through the muleta, a slow rhythm which protracts the danger, in which the lines and forms can be clearly seen.
8. Immobility should be preserved during the pass

and, if possible, during the series. Only the arm guiding the cloth may move as the body turns with the bull; the feet are motionless. This is true of the classic passes. There are passes, such as the *molinete,* in which the man must spin, but he should do so within narrow limits.

9. The horns should not touch the muleta, which must draw, lead, command.

10. Above all, the muleta must bring the bull past the man. The bull must not merely run in front of the matador as the cloth swings to the side. The matador must oblige, guide the charge, through the correct choice of terrain, the proper stance, the careful use of the muleta. In a continuous line, the muleta must attract the bull, control the charge, and recall the bull for the next pass.

Natural: Classic pass made with the muleta in the left hand. Except with a very bad bull, the natural should be seen in a faena worthy of respect. The natural is the simplest pass, the one pass which forbids the trick, the spinning and turning behind which the matador can hide his cowardice and ignorance. For this reason the aficionado will often shout, *"Izquierda* (left)," demanding to see the natural, when he wishes to judge the matador. The pass derives its name from the natural sweep of the arm. Juan Belmonte gave the natural facing the bull. Drawing the bull directly toward his body, he would give the bull an exit to his left. The public was certain Belmonte would be killed, and after being wounded and thrown countless times he changed his style and half faced the bull. Manolete gave the natural completely profiled to the bull with an elegance and dignity which none of his imitators have been able to copy. Belmonte's style involves more inherent control, but it is rarely seen. Antonio Ordóñez will, however, impose his control, half facing the bull in a series of naturals, and give the crowd a lesson and a performance to remember.

Novillada: Bullfight in which bulls between three and four years of age are killed. Picadors appear in the novillada.

Novillero: Killer of novillos. Some novilleros with great cartel are paid more than many matadors.

Novillo: A bull between three and four years old, sometimes fattened up to look like a mature bull and made to appear in a corrida.

Pablo Romero: Famous breed of bulls from Andalucía, known for their great strength.

Pase de pecho: One of the classic muleta passes. The matador stands with his back to the bull, somewhat in profile, the muleta held in his left hand. He receives the charge on his left and, as the animal reaches the cloth, the matador raises the muleta above the horns, forcing the bull past his chest. This pass is most often used to terminate a series of naturals. The *pase de pecho* frees the matador from the bull by giving the animal a way out of the encounter. The *pase de pecho* can also be made with the right hand.

Paseo: Entrance and passage across the arena by the toreros. Simple identification of the matadors can be made if one knows the order of names as they appear on the posters, billboards, etc. The top name, that of the senior matador, is at the head of the left column of toreros. The second name is at the head of the right column and that of the youngest at the head of the center column. Seniority dates from the alternativa, not from birth or popularity. In the paseo, the matadors are followed by their respective cuadrillas. They proceed until they are beneath the President's box, bow, and enter the *callejón.*

Pedresina: Muleta pass created by the matador Pedres, a recent phenomenon who flared up quickly, made a fortune, and went down quickly.

Peto: Mattress which protects the horse from obvious wounds, and which allows the picadors to assassinate the bulls if their matador orders it. The *peto* has been obligatory by law since 1928.

Pic: Lance used by the picador; see *Vara.*

Picador: Torero mounted on horseback. The picador is the only torero for whom strength is an absolute necessity. His role is to place the pic squarely in the *morillo* (tossing muscle between neck and shoulder) and hold the bull until the matador makes the *quite.*

Quite: The act of drawing the bull away from the man (or horse) upon whom he has fixed his attention and is charging or actually wounding. The *quite* is almost always made with the cape. It can, however, be made with the muleta or with the body itself. As the *quite* is an act in which one man attempts to save the life of another, there are no rules concerning its execution, and in this sense it is purely functional. *Quite* also refers to the taking of the bull away from the picador, whether or not the picador and/or horse are in danger, in order to create a series of passes between the pics. The *quite* following the first pic is made by the matador who will kill the bull, the other *quites* according to seniority.

Semental: Seed bull whose life is spent on the plains in the sun and whose sole function is to father other bulls. It is said that a bull derives courage from the mother and strength from the father. Semental bulls are very carefully selected.

Suerte: Luck. The word *suerte* is also used to refer to any action or group of actions in the bull ring. *Suerte de varas* refers to the act of pic-ing the bull. *Suerte de banderillas* refers to the placing of the banderillas, *suerte suprema* to the act of killing. A single complete pass will also be referred to as a *suerte,* as will a series of passes.

Temple: Used in reference to the motion given to either the capote or the muleta by the matador. A pass is said to have *temple* if the cloth is moved gracefully, slowly, in harmony with the bull's charge. (The verb *templar* means to soften, to temper, to allay, to moderate).

Temporada: The bullfight season. In Spain the *temporada* begins slowly in March with a few fights, gathers momentum, and is at its height in July, August and September. In October there is one big feria, in Zaragoza in honor of the Virgen del Pilar, which marks the end of the Spanish season. In the Western Hemisphere the important bullfights occur in the winter.

Tienta: The testing of the calves on the bull ranches, usually in the spring, in order to determine their bravery, strength and endurance.

Torero: Bullfighter. Anyone who faces a bull and is paid for it.

Toro: Bull. Used correctly to speak of a mature animal over four years of age. With age, a bull becomes more dangerous. When he reaches six or seven, it becomes virtually impossible to deceive him.

Toril: The gate and corridor from which the bull emerges when entering the arena.

Traje de luces: Traditional dress worn by toreros. Literally, suit of lights. The *traje de luces* worn by a matador weighs almost twenty pounds and is lavishly decorated in gold, rarely in silver. The banderillero's costume is as ornate as the matador's in every respect except that it is never embroidered with gold. The costume worn by the matador or banderillero is of silk and may be of any color. An individual matador may have as many as twenty costumes.

Vara: Wooden lance used by the picador. Between ten feet three inches and ten feet ten inches long, it is armed with a sharp pyramidal steel point one inch long, which is set into the shaft. For three inches immediately above the steel point, the wood is wrapped with heavy cord. A circular metal guard prevents more than these first four inches from penetrating the thick muscles of the *morillo;* that is, the guard protects the bull unless the picador twists and turns the pic in such a manner as to make the guard enter the wound against all established rules. The size of the wound that can be inflicted by the modern pic and the existence of the *peto* permit the bulls to be punished far more severely than before. The pic is the vital weapon that brings the bull's head down, thus permitting the matador to kill according to the rules. The President of the corrida regulates the number of pics which are given, usually three or four.

Vergüenza: Shame, self-respect. *"Sin vergüenza"*—without shame—is the most common insult for a cowardly or ignorant torero.

Verónica: Pass made with the capote held in both hands by the matador. The one classic capote pass which exists. The verónica will almost invariably be the first pass made by the matador when he confronts the bull. As with all passes made with either the capote or muleta, the verónica must exist in a linked series. The matador stands profiled or partly facing the bull. As the bull charges, the cloth is swept to one side, by the left arm if the bull is to exit from the encounter on the matador's left, or by the right arm if to the right. A verónica to the left is followed by one to the right, and then to the left, and then to the right as often as the matador deems necessary and possible. This series is invariably terminated by the media verónica—half verónica—a pass which begins like the verónica but in which the arm that extends the capote, instead of sweeping outward, cuts sharply back toward the matador's hip, swirling the capote quickly away from the bull's vision. This maneuver stops the bull's charge short and fixes him in place, permitting the matador to walk away. The verónica will also be seen during the *quites,* though often in the *quites* some of the fancier passes will be made as the matadors compete with one another.

About the Author

Peter Buckley is both a writer and a photographer. He is the author of a notable series for children, "The Around The World Today Books." Each of these tells the story of an actual child living in a particular country today. His pictures have appeared in *Life, Harper's Bazaar, Esquire*, and other magazines.

Born in New York City in 1925, he went to school in London, Paris, Rome, Geneva, and Vienna. He is a graduate of Princeton and also studied at the University of Paris. During World War II he served in Europe as a member of the U.S. Army's Counter Intelligence Corps. He saw his first bullfights at the age of eight and has followed them ever since. He estimates that he traveled about 10,000 miles back and forth across Spain (often in the company of the matadors and their cuadrillas) to gather the material for BULLFIGHT.